MW00532061

KEY TO COMMON WOODY LANDSCAPE PLANTS IN THE MIDWEST

by

BENTON M. STIDD and ROBERT D. HENRY

WESTERN ILLINOIS UNIVERSITY

ISBN 0-87563-508-3

Publishing by

Stipes Publishing L.L.C.
204 W. University Ave.
Champaign, Illinois 61820

CONTENTS

INTRODUCTION 1
HOW TO USE THE KEYS 4
KEY TO COMMON WOODY LANDSCAPE PLANTS IN THE MIDWEST 6
KEY TO ANGIOSPERMS 6
KEY TO GYMNOSPERMS 66
GLOSSARY 76
SCIENTIFIC NAME INDEX 87
COMMON NAME INDEX 102
REFERENCES 118

INTRODUCTION

Current popular manuals of woody landscape plants (such as Dirr's *Manual of Woody Landscape Plants*) contain much useful information about each species or cultivar including descriptions of leaf, stem, flower and fruit. Taxa are often arranged alphabetically by genus and if one knows the identity of a plant, it is a relatively easy task to locate the species and acquire additional information. If however, one does not know the identity of the plant, it is often a daunting task to flip from page to page attempting to match the plant in question with a leaf sketch or verbal description. Comprehensive botanical manuals exist such as Bailey's *Manual of Cultivated Plants* but the sheer bulk of the volume and number of species included deters use by the uninitiated. Moreover, such manuals often base their keys on reproductive characters which limit their usefulness. It was this state of affairs that prompted us to write this manual.

The major features of this manual are:

1. The species included are restricted to common woody landscape plants one is likely to encounter in the midwest. Woody plants are those trees and shrubs with secondary growth of their stems and trunks that adds to their diameter over the years.

2. Vegetative characters of plants in full summer foliage have been used as the primary diagnostic basis for identification. Because so many species of landscape plants resemble one another very closely, we sometimes resort to features such as bud scales or stipule scars that require close observation—often done best with a hand lens or a dissecting microscope. A variety of other problems may be encountered such as leaves appearing whorled in early spring that later, after branch elongation, will appear alternate.

3. We have added, after the colon in some couplet statements, flower and fruit characters. These reproductive characters are not necessarily diagnostic or contrasting but are added to help confirm the identity of the unknown plant based on its vegetative characters. If flower or fruit characters are present they will help in confirming identity but one does not have to have them to be able to use the key.

4. Abbreviations used throughout the key are:

   Flr(s) = flower(s)
   Frt(s) = fruit(s)
   lf = leaf
   lvs = leaves
   lflet(s) = leaflet(s)
   yr(s) = year(s)

5. The key is divided into two major sections, i.e.,

   Angiosperms = Flowering Plants

   Gymnosperms = Plants without flowers but reproducing by naked seeds in cones. This group includes the familiar Pines, Firs, Spruces, Junipers, etc. Most of these have scale-like or needle-like leaves and retain them throughout the year.

6. Plant names (both scientific and common) for the most part follow those recognized by Dirr in his *Manual of Woody Landscape Plants.* See Dirr for a greater range of common names and synonyms.

7. The key is written to the species level. In a few cases, *Malus* for example, a key to species is not attempted. Neither have we attempted to distinguish among cultivars at the subspecific level except in the case of some of the extremely common ones. We recommend that the key be

used to determine the species and if one wants to know the cultivar, consult the listing and brief description found in Dirr's Manual or other similar work. For certain genera (*Malus, Rhododendron,* etc), where many cultivars exist, one will have to consult more specialized references such as those provided in the reference section of this manual.

8. A species can be found by either common or scientific name by use of the Common Name Index or the Scientific Name Index. Each index is cross referenced. Both the page number and couplet number are provided for each entry.
9. Meanings of unfamiliar terms can be found in the Glossary.

USERS COMMENTS WELCOME

We would appreciate comments from users where the keys are found to be mistaken or inadequate. Send comments to Department of Biological Sciences, Western Illinois University, Macomb, IL 61455.

HOW TO USE THE KEYS

The key is dichotomous meaning that it consists of consecutively numbered couplets (each member of a couplet lettered a and b). The members of each couplet consist of opposing or contrasting statements. These statements are based upon midsummer vegetative (non-reproductive) characters but reproductive characters have been included (after the colon) as additional clues and will be useful if the plant is in the reproductive phase.

To identify a plant start with the unnumbered couplet that separates angiosperms from gymnosperms at the top of page 6. If the plant is a gymnosperm go to couplet number one on page 66 and if an angiosperm go to couplet number 1 on the same page.

For example, suppose the plant to be identified is an angiosperm. Starting with couplet numbered 1 on page 6, read each statement (i.e. 1a or 1b) and determine which statement agrees with the plant you are attempting to identify. It is important that several plant specimens be observed so your choice is correct and accounts for any character variation that occurs. The statement that you choose leads to further information at the extreme right of the page: either the scientific name of the plant or the number of the next couplet to which you proceed. Here the process is repeated and you continue in this manner until you arrive at a scientific name.

The glossary should be used to help with terms. If you do not arrive at a correct identification or are unsure of your identification, re-key being sure your observations are accurate. In case both statements of a couplet seem to apply (as often occurs in closely related or very similar plants) keying under both members of the couplet will usually reveal which couplet choice works out to the correct identification.

There are two indexes: one to common names and one to scientific names. Both indexes are cross-referenced to the common and scientific names.

KEY TO COMMON WOODY LANDSCAPE PLANTS IN THE MIDWEST

IF PLANT IS A GYMNOSPERM (has seeds borne in cones—no flrs nor fruits, has needle-like or scale-like lvs)

GO TO NUMBER 1 ON PAGE 66

IF PLANT IS AN ANGIOSPERM (has flrs and frts during the life cycle, has broad lvs with net venation)

GO TO NUMBER 1 BELOW

KEY TO ANGIOSPERMS

1a. Leaves opposite or whorled (avoid young stems with unelongated internodes) 2
1b. Leaves alternate 143

2a. Leaves whorled 3
2b. Leaves opposite 7

3a. Leaves small, needle-like: Flrs small, often nodding, 4 parted, urn-shaped . . . . *Erica*
3b. Leaves broad, flat—not needle-like 4

4a. Leaves 3 or more inches wide: Frts long & narrow, more or less 1 ft long 5
4b. Leaves up to 1 1/2" wide: Frts not elongated, much smaller 6

5a. Lvs 6–12" long, lf tip long acuminate, crushed lvs scentless; seed with fringed hairs on margin; habit taller than wide: Corolla with few purple spots . . . . . *Catalpa speciosa*
5b. Lvs 4–8" (10") long, lf tip short pointed, crushed lvs unpleasant odor; seeds with tufted hairs; habit spreading/rounded: Corolla with numerous purple spots . . . . *Catalpa bignonioides*

6a. Height over 1 foot; shrub or small tree, attractive smooth grey bark: Flrs in July thru September in 6–8" open panicles, 6 petals, flr up to 1 1/2" across . . . . *Lagerstroemia indica*

6b. Height 1 foot or less, ground cover: Flrs May thru July in dense heads of small flrs subtended by showy petal-like bracts, white . . . . *Cornus canadensis*

7a. Leaves simple 8

7b. Leaves compound 44

8a. Scale-like leaves, 1/8" or less long: Flrs similar to *Erica* (see 3a) . . . . *Calluna vulgaris*

8b. Leaves over 1/8" long 9

9a. Trees or shrubs 16

9b. Ground covers or vines 10

10a. Leaves less than 1/4" wide; Low growing evergreen shrub: Flrs tiny, not showy . . . . *Paxistima canbyi*

10b. Leaves more than 1/4" wide 11

11a. Ground cover, evergreen: Flowers blue 12

11b. Vine: Flowers not blue 13

12a. Lvs up to 1 1/2" long; lf base rounded or cuneate; plants 3–6" high: Calyx lobes glabrous . . . . *Vinca minor*

12b. Lvs up to 3" long; some lvs nearly cordate; plants 12–18" high: Calyx lobes with hairs . . . . *Vinca major*

13a. Lvs entire: Flrs showy, frts fleshy, not splitting . . . 14

13b. Lvs serrate/crenate; silvery-white veins common: Frts not showy, greenish, 4 parted, splitting to reveal orange color . . . . *Euonymus fortunei*

14a. Upper lvs connate at base; plants viny: Frts red 15

14b. Upper lvs not connate; plants viny: Frts black . . . . *Lonicera japonica*

15a. Stems red/purple: Flrs pink-purple on outside . . . . *Lonicera × heckrottii*
15b. Stems straw colored: Flrs orange-red to red on outside . . . . *Lonicera sempervirens*

16a. Trees 17
16b. Shrubs 61

17a. Leaves lobed 18
17b. Leaves unlobed 33

18a. Lvs with 3 forward pointing lobes in upper half of leaf: Frts winged—Maples 19
18b. Lvs with 3 or more lobes but not restricted to upper half of leaf: Frts winged—Maples . . . 21

19a. Lf entire or slightly and irregularly serrate . . . . *Acer buergeranum*
19b. Lvs regularly serrulate or more prominently toothed 20

20a. Bark on branches with greenish white stripes: Flrs borne in May on 4–6" long racemes . . . . *Acer pensylvanicum*
20b. Bark not striped . . . . *Acer rubrum*

21a. Lvs with middle (terminal) lobe much larger than the two lateral lobes 22
21b. Lvs 5 or more lobed and of more or less equal size 23

22a. Lf tip long acuminate; buds 1/8" long and reddish brown . . . . *Acer ginnala*
22b. Lf tip not long acuminate; buds larger and brownish black . . . . . *Acer tataricum*

23a. Milky sap can be pressed from severed petioles . . . 24
23b. Milky sap not present 27

24a. Buds 1/4 to 3/8" long, plump 25
24b. Buds less than 1/4" long, not plump 26

25a. Lvs truncate at base, up to 5" wide, lobes not toothed: Nutlets about as long as the wing, wings spreading about 90 degrees from each other . . . . *Acer truncatum*

25b. Lvs with basal lobes (not truncate), up to 7" wide, lobes toothed: Wing distinctly longer than nutlet, wings spreading at 180 degrees . . . . *Acer platanoides*

26a. Lvs 4–6" wide, 3–5" long, petioles 4–7" long, lobes acuminate . . . . *Acer miyabei*

26b. Lvs 2–4" long & wide, petiole up to 4" long, lobes rounded to acute . . . . *Acer campestre*

27a. Branch tips with paired buds; If lobes usually more than 5 28

27b. Branch tips with 3 buds (central one larger than laterals) 29

28a. Lvs glabrous, generally deeply incised . . . . *Acer palmatum*

28b. Lvs pubescent particularly on veins below, lvs less deeply incised . . *Acer japonicum*

29a. Terminal buds sharp pointed 30

29b. Terminal buds not sharp pointed 31

30a. Lateral lobes of lvs drooping, stipules (nubbins to small lvs) variably present; buds lateral to the terminal bud up to 3/4 the length of the terminal one . . . . *Acer nigrum*

30b. Lateral lobes not drooping, stipules not present; lateral buds up to 1/2 as long as terminal . . . . *Acer saccharum*

31a. Buds 1/4" or more long, plump, green; lvs 3–6" wide, shallow lobed, coarse, leathery, fall color none: Flrs borne in May with lvs and in pendulous 2–4" clusters .... *Acer pseudoplatanus*

31b. Buds < 1/4", reddish; lvs not leathery: Flrs before lvs, not long clusters 32

32a. Lvs deeply lobed, sinuses usually more than half way to base or midrib, sinuses entire: Flrs without petals, pedicels remaining short .... *Acer saccharinum*

32b. Sinuses less than half way to midrib, sinuses toothed: Flrs with petals, pedicels elongating with age ..... *Acer rubrum*

Acer × freemanii is a hybrid between *A. rubrum* and *A. saccharinum* that often exhibits a mixture of features of the two parents.

33a. Lf margin (edge) entire 34

33b. Lf margin toothed or crenate 41

34a. Lf large, average 6" (3–10) wide; average 8" (4–12) long 35

34b. Lvs distinctly smaller, less than 4" wide 36

35a. Pith chambered, fruit 1–2" long: Flrs showy, pale blue, 2" long, May; flr buds conspicuous in winter .... *Paulownia tomentosa*

35b. Pith solid, fruit 6" or longer, pod-like: Flrs white .... Go back to *Catalpa* 5

36a. Lvs sessile or nearly so (see 6a) .... *Lagerstroemia indica*

36b. Lvs on petioles 1/4" or longer 37

37a. Lf scars touching, not conspicuously raised; lf veins approach but do not intersect the margin: Flowers and fruits in dense clusters *or* flat-topped clusters up to 3" broad, frts red—Dogwood 38

37b. Leaf scars not touching, scars raised: Flowers or fruits in open panicles, frts blue 40

38a. Lvs 3–6" long, petioles 1/4–3/4" long; flr buds flattened biscuit-shaped: Flr clusters subtended by large showy bracts . . . . *Cornus florida*

38b. Lvs up to 4", petioles 1/2" or less; flr buds not flattened nor biscuit-shaped 39

39a. Petioles 1/4–1/2"; lvs with tufts of hairs below at vein/midrib junction; flr buds globose at base with 2 silky scales forming pointed apex: Flr cluster subtended by large showy bracts . . . . *Cornus kousa*

39b. Petioles 1/4", lvs pilose but without tufts of hairs below; flr buds shaped like a hot-air balloon: Bracts small & yellow . . . *Cornus mas*

40a. Lvs oblongish (3–8"); not conspicuously leathery; flrs and frts on previous yrs wood, flrs white in 6–8" long panicles . . . . . *Chionanthus virginicus*

40b. Lvs smaller, rounder, leathery; flrs on current yrs growth, flrs white in 2–3" long panicles . . . . *Chionanthus retusus*

41a. Lf base cordate; 2 stubby spurs at each node: Flrs not showy; frts 3/4" long pods . . . . . . *Cercidiphyllum japonicum*

41b. Lf base not cordate 42

42a. Buds plump, greenish: Flrs small, greenish, not showy; frts pink to red, splitting to reveal orange color . . . . *Euonymus europaeus*

42b. Buds dark, brown or black or reddish: Flrs not showy; frts winged, not splitting 43

43a. Bud scales opposite, black:
Frts borne singly . . . . *Fraxinus excelsior* 'Hessei'

43b. Bud scales not opposite:
Frts in pairs . . . . *Acer tataricum*

44a. Lvs trifoliate or pinnately compound 45

44b. Lvs palmately compound 55

45a. Lvs trifoliate 46

45b. Lvs pinnate 47

46a. Lflets coarsly toothed to lobed,
attractive exfoliating bark:
Frts flat (samara) . . . . *Acer griseum*

46b. Lvs very finely toothed;
frts inflated (bladder-like
capsule) . . . . *Staphylea trifolia*

47a. Tree or shrub 48

47b. Vines 54

48a. Tree 49

48b. Shrub, pith solid white, large;
stems weak: Tiny white flrs
and fleshy purple frts in large
flat-topped clusters . . . . . *Sambucus canadensis*

49a. Lf scars nearly encircling bud;
no terminal bud, frts 1/2" diam
black drupes borne in 2–3"
long panicles . . . . *Phellodendron amurense*

49b. Lf scars not encircling bud,
terminal bud present, frt a samara 50

50a. Lf scars encircle stem and edges
meet; buds greenish/reddish; may be
some trifoliate lvs, lflets range
from unlobed to irregularly lobed;
stems often green and/or glaucous:
Samaras paired . . . . *Acer negundo*

50b. Lf scars not encircling stem, not
meeting, buds chocolate brown to buff:
Samaras single—Ash 51

51a. Young stems 4-sided; buds greyish . . . . *Fraxinus quadrangulata*
51b. Stems not angular 52

52a. Buds black . . . . *Fraxinus excelsior*
52b. Buds not black (dark brown) 53

53a. Lf scar straight across the top; vascular bundle scars forming a more or less closed C . . . . *Fraxinus pennsylvanica*
53b. Lf scar concave at top, partially encircling bud; vascular bundle scars forming an open C . . . . *Fraxinus americana*

54a. Lflets toothed: Flrs 2 1/2 to 3" long, trumpet-shaped, usually bright orange; frts 3–5" long pod . . . . *Campsis radicans*
54b. Lflets entire: Flrs 4–7" diameter, not trumpet-shaped, most purple; frts not pod-like, 1–2" long with elongate feathery style . . . *Clematis* × *jackmanii*

55a. Lflets deeply dissected giving fern-like appearance, less than 3/4" wide: Frts paired samaras . . . . *Acer palmatum* (dissected types)
55b. Lflets mostly toothed—not fern-like, 1" or wider: Frts spherical and not winged—Buckeyes and Horsechestnuts 56

56a. Buds resinous 57
56b. Buds not resinous 58

57a. Lflets predominantly 7, buds 1/2–3/4", dark brown, glabrous, flrs white with red or yellow splotches toward base . . . . *Aesculus hippocastanum*
57b. Lflets mostly 5, buds small and less sticky, flrs flesh colored to red . . . . *Aesculus* × *carnea*

58a. Buds gray-brown, lvs with moderately dense (gray) pubescence beneath; Broad spreading shrub to 12', flrs white .... *Aesculus parviflora*

58b. Buds not as above, lvs lightly pubescent to glabrous, trees or if shrub not widely spreading 59

59a. Lflet margins irregularly serrate: Flrs red .... *Aesculus pavia*

59b. Lflet margins uniformly & finely serrate: Flrs yellowish 60

60a. Bud scales keeled: Frts prickly . . *Aesculus glabra*

60b. Bud scales not keeled: Frts smooth .... *Aesculus flava (octandra)*

61a. Lvs toothed 62

61b. Lvs not toothed (entire) 104

62a. Some lvs over 6" long 63

62b. No lvs over 6" long 67

63a. Petioles less than 1/2" long: Flrs in elongate, tapering clusters .... *Buddleia davidii*

63b. Petioles 1/2" or longer: Flrs in globular clusters, usually white—*Hydrangea* 64

64a. Lvs lobed .... *Hydrangea quercifolia*

64b. Lvs not lobed 65

65a. Lvs to 6" long by 3" wide: Flr clusters less globular than other species .... *Hydrangea paniculata*

65b. Lvs larger, up to 8" long by 6" wide 66

66a. Lvs rounded or cordate at base, petioles to 3" long .... *Hydrangea arborescens*

66b. Lvs tapering at base into petiole, petioles to 1 1/4" long: Flrs often blue .... *Hydrangea macrophylla*

67a. Lf margin doubly serrate: Flrs with 4 white petals, 1–2" diam; frts jet black in clusters of 3–4 ..... *Rhodotypus scandens*
67b. Lf margin not doubly serrate 68

68a. Lines or hairs decurrent from nodes 69
68b. No internodal lines or hairs 70

69a. Four internodal lines of hairs: Flrs two-lipped, yellow .... *Diervilla sessilifolia*
69b. Two internodal lines of hairs: Flrs not two-lipped, not yellow .... *Weigela florida*

70a. Twigs with winged projections (reduced in some cultivars): Frts & seeds red/orange; excellent bright red to pink fall color ... *Euonymus alatus*
70b. Twigs not winged 71

71a. Vegetative buds without scales (naked, foliose) ... 72
71b. Vegetative buds with 2 or more scales 80

72a. Short paired lateral branches in same plane at nodes giving a fishbone effect: Flrs white, not fragrant, borne above and along horizontal branches creating a tiered effect .... *Viburnum plicatum* var. *tomentosum* (The Japanese Snowball Viburnum which has spherical clusters of white flrs belongs to this species.)
72b. Lateral branches not as above 73

73a. Some lvs over 5" long; lvs elongate/lanceolate ... 74
73b. Lvs 5 " or less; lvs broader, mostly ovate 75

74a. Lvs up to 2 1/2" wide, strongly rugose above, evergreen: Flrs in 3–4" flat-topped clusters ... *Viburnum rhytidophyllum*
74b. Lvs broader, less rugose, not evergreen: Flrs & frts in 4–8" flat topped clusters .. *Viburnum × rhytidophylloides*

75a. Petioles generally 1/2" or more long 76
75b. Petioles 1/2" or less 77

76a. Lvs up to 5" long and up to 4" wide, wrinkled above: Flrs in 3–5" wide flat-topped clusters . . . . *Viburnum lantana*
76b. Lvs up to 4" long and up to 2 1/2" wide, not wrinkled: Flrs in 3–8" globose clusters . . . . *Viburnum macrocephalum*

77a. Lvs dull above 78
77b. Lvs lustrous above 79

78a. Lvs dark green above: Stamen filaments shorter than anthers . . *Viburnum carlesii*
78b. Lvs bluish gray-green: Stamen filaments longer than anthers . . *Viburnum* × *juddii*

79a. Lvs usually more glossy than *carlcephalum:* Flower clusters 3 1/2" across . . . . *Viburnum* × *burkwoodii*
79b. Lvs less shiny than *burkwoodii:* Flower clusters up to 5′ across . . . . *Viburnum* × *carlcephalum*

80a. Vegetative buds small and not readily observable; stem angular: Flrs white and often fragrant; old fruit capsules persistent, dry, colorless, glabrous and present most of the year, 4 parted 81
80b. Buds larger and detectable: Fruits not as above 82

81a. Lvs up to 4" long, slight hairiness on veins below: Flr parts not doubled . . . . *Philadelphus coronarius*
81b. Lvs up to 3" and villous beneath: Flrs mostly doubled . . . . . . *Philadelphus* × *virginalis* ('Minnesota Snowflake' is a common cultivar of this species)

82a. Buds imbricate 83
82b. Buds valvate 97

83a. Lvs glabrous on upper surface 84
83b. Lvs pubescent on both surfaces 92

84a. Lower lf surface glabrous:
Corolla 4 parted 85
84b. Lower lf surface with pubescence,
at least on veins 91

85a. Young stems green or olive-green 86
85b. Young stems not green (various shades
of brown, gray, yellowish):
Flrs showy before lvs, yellow—Forsythia 89

86a. Lf serrations restricted to
upper 1/2 of leaf and up to
6" long; pith chambered:
Flrs yellow . . . . *Forsythia viridissima*
86b. Lf serrations or crenations not
restricted to upper half, leaves smaller 87

87a. Lf margin crenate; stem turning gray-
brown second year; buds plump; plant
to 30' and free standing:
Flrs greenish . . . . *Euonymus europaeus*
87b. Lf margins serrate; plants much smaller 88

88a. Pith chambered including nodes:
Flrs yellow . . *Forsythia viridissima* 'Bronxensis'
88b. Pith sometimes hollow or excavated
but not chambered; veins light or
silvery; stems often with patches
of roots (A large and variable
group): Flrs greenish . . . . . . *Euonymus fortunei*

89a. Stems hollow, solid at nodes; long
pendulous branches . . . *Forsythia suspensa* var. *seiboldii*
89b. Stems not hollow; pith chambered 90

90a. Lvs up to 5" long, lvs oblong lanceolate;
stems squarish . . . . *Forsythia* × *intermedia*
90b. Lvs up to 3 1/2" long, ovate or
broad ovate; stems rounded . . . *Forsythia ovata*

91a. Lf margin coarsely and regularly dentate; broadly ovate, to 4 1/2" long: Flrs in long stalked clusters up to 4" wide; frts blue/black . . . . *Viburnum dentatum*

91b. Lf margin remotely and slightly denticulate; narrowly ovate, to 6" long: Flr clusters up to 2" wide, short stalks; frts red . . . . *Viburnum setigerum*

92a. Lvs with stellate pubescence: Flrs mostly white—*Deutzia* 93

92b. Lf pubescence not stellate 96

93a. Lvs lightly pubescent below 94

93b. Lvs densely pubescent below, rough to touch: Petals valvate in bud, some cultivars with double flrs 95

94a. Lvs up to 3" long, tips of serrations glandular; bark yellowish gray-brown, not exfoliating; commonly 2–4'(6) high: Petals valvate in bud . . . . . *Deutzia gracilis*

94b. Lvs up to 4" long; bark brown and exfoliating on older branches; 5–7' tall: Petals imbricate in bud . . . . *Deutzia × lemoinei*

95a. Lf margin finely crenate or serrate; bark brown: Calyx teeth as long as calyx tube; styles usually 4 . . . . *Deutzia × magnifica*

95b. Lf margin crenate or dentate; bark red-brown: Calyx teeth shorter than tube; styles usually 3 . . . . *Deutzia scabra*

96a. Lvs 1–3" long, petiole 1/8" long; stem villose at first, later glabrous: Flrs in pairs, flaring & bell-shaped, pink with yellow throat . . . . *Kolkwitzia amabilis*

96b. Lvs 2–5" long, petiole 1/4–3/4" long; stems hispid, orange lenticels: Flrs small in flat-topped clusters, white; frts a reddish drupe, not bristly . . . . *Viburnum dilatatum*

97a. Lvs lobed—Viburnums 98
97b. Lvs unlobed—Viburnums 100

98a. Some petioles up to 1 3/4"; stems with somewhat corky bark; middle lobe of leaf often elongate with two short lateral lobes: Anthers purple .. *Viburnum sargentii*
98b. Petioles up to 1" long: Anthers yellow 99

99a. Glands on petiole concave .... *Viburnum opulus*
99b. Glands on petiole domed .... *Viburnum trilobum*

100a. Lvs up to 6" long, stellate pubescent beneath, disagreeable odor when crushed; habit large and coarse among Viburnums: Very showy in flr and frt ...... *Viburnum sieboldii*
100b. Lvs 4" or less, not stellate pubescent ... 101

101a. Lvs acuminate; petiole up to 1" and winged with wavy margin: Flr buds up to 1" long, bulbous at base .... *Viburnum lentago*
101b. Lvs acutish; petioles shorter and not winged ... 102

102a. Buds yellow or yellow brown .... *Viburnum cassinoides*
102b. Buds not yellow 103

103a. Veins impressed; petioles purplish; lvs pubescent-scabrous at least early on; bud scales decussate .... *Viburnum farreri*
103b. Veins not impressed; petiole reddish; lvs glabrous or nearly so; buds valvate .... *Viburnum prunifolium*

104a. Lvs with small nearly transparent dots (hold up to light, use hand lens), often with clusters of smaller lvs at base of larger lvs: Flrs yellow with numerous stamens—*Hypericum* 105
104b. Lvs without dots 107

105a. Branches 4 angled, lateral branches often only 2 sided: Styles 5; capsule 5 furrowed . . . . *Hypericum kalmianum*

105b. Branches only two-sided: Styles 3; frt capsules 3 parted 106

106a. Lvs glossy above: Flrs 1" or less across; frts 1/2" long . . *Hypericum prolificum*

106b. Lvs not glossy: Flrs more than 1" across; frts 3/4" long . . . . *Hypericum frondosum*

107a. Lvs yellow . . . . *Ligustrum* × *vicaryi*

107b. Lvs not yellow 108

108a. Lvs 1" long or less: Flrs small, inconspicuous, creamy in axillary or terminal clusters 109

108b. Lvs (at least some) longer 110

109a. Stems distinctly 4 angled, grooved between each pair of lvs, green; lvs usually broadest above the middle . . . . *Buxus microphylla*

109b. Stems squarish but not distinctly so, green; lvs broadest below the middle . . . . *Buxus sempervirens*

110a. Twigs with distinctly pleasant odor when bruised: Flrs dark reddish brown, 2" wide; frts obovate and about 2 1/2 long, persistent . . *Calycanthus floridus*

110b. Twigs not aromatic: Flrs and frts not as above 111

111a. Buds naked, foliose 112

111b. Buds scaled 114

112a. Some lvs up to 5" long: Flrs in flat-topped clusters; fruits present 113

112b. Lvs up to 4" long: Flrs in hemispherical clusters; frts absent . . . . . . *Viburnum macrocephalum*

113a. Lvs up to 2 1/2" wide, strongly rugose above, evergreen (See couplet 74) . . . . *Viburnum rhytidophyllum*

113b. Lvs broader, less rugose, not evergreen . . . . *Viburnum × rhytidophylloides*

114a. Buds with 2 valvate scales; lateral veins approach but curve away from leaf margin—Dogwoods 115

114b. Buds imbricate with more than 2 scales . . 123

115a. Large axillary (at lateral vein junctions with midrib) tufts of tawny hairs: Flrs and frt clusters borne on 2–2 1/2" long stalks; frt cluster spherical; showy bracts with pointed tips . . . . *Cornus kousa*

115b. Axillary hairs not present: Flr stalks shorter; frt cluster not spherical 116

116a. Pubescence appressed 118

116b. Pubescence not appressed: Showy bracts absent 117

117a. Lvs villous on both surfaces; pith white: Frts purplish-black . . . . *Cornus sanguinea*

117b. Lvs glabrous above; pith brown: Frts blue often with white blotches . . *Cornus amomum*

118a. Petioles about 1/4" long: Flr buds axillary, large shaped like a hot-air balloon; flrs yellow, March; bracts not showy . . . . *Cornus mas*

118b. Petioles (at least some) 1/2" or longer: Flr buds not as above 119

119a. Twigs yellow: Bracts not showy; frts white . . . . . *Cornus sericea* 'Flaviramea'

119b. Twigs not yellow 120

120a. Twigs uniformly bright red to dark red: Bracts not showy; frts white (bluish) 121

120b. Twigs gray, brown, or greenish to purplish 122

121a. Lf surface rugose, small blisters between veins, feels somewhat rough; lvs 2 to 4 1/2" long, acute; branches upright . . . . *Cornus alba*

121b. Lf surface smoother to eye and touch, no blisters; up to 5" long, acuminate; branches bowed, often rooting . . . . (*Cornus stolonifera*) *Cornus sericea*

- 122a. Lvs 3–6" long to 3" wide: Flr buds erect, large, biscuit shaped; bracts showy; frts red . . . . *Cornus florida*
- 122b. Lvs 2–4" long to 2" wide: Flr buds not enlarged and not conspicuous; bracts not showy; frts white . . . . *Cornus racemosa*

123a. Twig ends often with a pair of plump buds resulting in a forked branching pattern: Petals 4; mature frts brown, dry, 1/2 to 3/4" long—Lilacs 124

123b. Twig ends with one bud 128

- 124a. Bark (on stems) reddish brown to brown with prominent horizontal lenticels (cherry-like). Often a tree at maturity: Flrs white in 6–12" long clusters . . . . . . *Syringa reticulata*
- 124b. Bark not as above; shrubs: Showy infloresence, usually lavender, petals 4—Lilacs 125

125a. Lvs glabrous 126

125b. Lvs pubescent below (at least on veins) 127

- 126a. Lvs up to 5" long; lf bases cordate/truncate . . . . *Syringa vulgaris*
- 126b. Lvs up to 3" long; lf bases cuneate . . . . *Syringa × chinensis*

127a. Lvs up to 2" long; new lvs with purplish margin . . . . *Syringa meyeri*

127b. Lvs up to 5" long . . . . *Syringa patula*

128a. Buds superposed; lf scars with 3 distinct bundle scars: 5 petals in 2 groups; frts fleshy red berry—Honeysuckles 129

128b. Buds not superposed; bundle scars appearing as a horizontal line 134

129a. Lvs roundish, stiff and leatherish; pith white: Flrs early before the lvs . . . . *Lonicera fragrantissima*

129b. Lvs not as above; pith brown or hollow: Flrs with lvs 130

130a. Lf tips acuminate . . . . *Lonicera maackii*

130b. Lf tips not acuminate 131

131a. Young stems glabrous; some lvs subcordate at base; often infected with Russian aphid causing scattered tufted branches with wilted lvs . . . . *Lonicera tatarica*

131b. Young stems pubescent; lvs rounded or cuneate at base 132

132a. Axillary buds long pointed, heavily gray/brown pubescent; pith brown, excavated 133

132b. Buds small, blunt; stems hollow . . . . *Lonicera morrowii*

133a. Plants 6–10′; foliage blue-green . . . . *Lonicera xylosteum*

133b. Plants 3–6′; foliage grey-green; retains lower branches (often included in *L. xylosteum*) . . . *Lonicera* × *xylosteoides*

134a. Some lvs up to 4" or more long 135

134b. Lvs up to 2 1/2" 137

135a. Lvs up to 7" long: Flr clusters often in 3 groups at end of shoot and borne on current growth; anthers protruding from corolla . . . . *Syringa villosa*

135b. Lvs up to 4" long 136

136a. Lvs glabrous, leathery, very dark green: Flrs small, white . . . . *Ligustrum japonicum*

136b. Lvs pubescent on veins below, not leathery, dark green: Flrs lavender/pink, anthers not protruding . . . . *Syringa sweginzowii*

137a. Lvs roundish/ovate; lf scars shriveled at edge: Frts berry-like drupe, white-red/purple . . 138

137b. Lvs oblongish; lf scars not shriveled: Frts black/purple 141

138a. Petioles less than 1/8" long; pith solid . . . 139

138b. Petioles more than 1/8"; pith excavated/hollow: Frts white 140

139a. Lvs up to about 3/4" long; young stems and petioles red: Frts not solid colored (pinkish) . . . . *Symphoricarpos × chenaultii*

139b. Lvs up to 1 1/4": Frts solid red/purple . . . *Symphoricarpos orbiculatus*

140a. Some lvs lobed . . . . . . *Symphoricarpos albus*

140b. No lvs lobed . . . . *Symphoricarpos albus*

141a. Lvs glabrous both sides; lvs up to 2 1/2" long and up to 5/8" wide: Corolla tube not longer than corolla lobes . . . . *Ligustrum vulgare*

141b. Lvs pubescent below; lvs wider: Corolla tube much longer than lobes 142

142a. Some lvs obovate, pubescence below not necessarily restricted to midrib; habit spreading, broadest at top: Calyx pubescent . . . . *Ligustrum obtusifolium*

142b. Lvs not obovate, pubescence below restricted to midrib; habit dense, upright; weakly pyramidal (narrrow at top): Calyx glabrous . . . . *Ligustrum amurense*

143a. Lvs simple 181
143b. Lvs compound 144

144a. Lvs pinnately compound 151
144b. Lvs palmately compound or trifoliate 145

145a. Lvs palmately compound (with more than 3 lflets) 149
145b. Lvs trifoliate 146

146a. Lflets toothed 147
146b. Lflets entire: Flrs yellow 148

147a. Stems with prickles—Roses . . . . *Rosa*
147b. Stems without prickles; crushed lvs & twigs with pleasant odor . . . . *Rhus aromatica*

148a. Lflets up to 3/4" long; 5–6′ tall, distinctly shrubby: Flrs borne along stem; frts sessile and hairy only along margins . . . . *Cytisus scoparius*
148b. Lflets 1" or more long; 12–15′ small tree or large shrub: Flrs in 6–10" terminal pendulous racemes; frts stalked and pubescent . . . . *Laburnum × watereri*

149a. Stems armed: Flrs small greenish-white borne in a spherical cluster on a 2–4" stalk . . . . . . *Acanthopanax sieboldianus*
149b. Stems unarmed 150

150a. Lflets toothed; clinging by tendrils: Flrs greenish (yellowish) white . . . . *Parthenocissus quinquefolia*
150b. Lflets entire; tendrils absent: Flrs purplish . . . . *Akebia quinata*

151a. Vines: Flrs violet-blue . . . . *Wisteria florabunda*
151b. Not Vines 152

152a. Even pinnate; usually an erect shrub: Flrs yellow; 2" long pod . . . . *Caragana arborescens*
152b. Odd pinnate 153

153a. Lflets entire 154
153b. Lflets toothed 165

154a. Shrubs: Flrs showy, mostly yellow or small greenish-yellow 155
154b. Trees 158

155a. Lvs small, less than 3", lflets 1/2–1" long, lflets 3–7: Flrs showy yellow, 3/4–1 1/4" across (some cultivars with red or other colors) . . . . *Potentilla fruticosa*
155b. Lvs large, 8" or more long, lflets 2 or more inches long, lflets 9 or more: Flrs much smaller and not showy; frts in conspicuous dense dark red terminal pyramidal clusters 156

156a. Rachis winged . . . . *Rhus copallina*
156b. Rachis not winged 157

157a. Stems hairy . . . . *Rhus typhina*
157b. Stems glabrous . . . . *Rhus glabra*

158a. Lflets 20 or more: Flrs white; frts large flattened pods 159
158b. Lflets 19 or less 160

159a. Lvs over 1 foot long, bipinnate, lflets ovate with acuminate tips: Frts up to 2" wide, not twisted, thick, stout, pulpy . . . . *Gymnocladus dioicus*
159b. Lvs under 1 foot long, both once or twice pinnate, lflets narrower with acute-rounded tips: Frts up to 1" wide, irregularly twisted, thin, not pulpy . . . . *Gleditsia triacanthos* var. *inermis*

160a. Terminal lflet blade more than 4" long . . . 161
160b. Terminal lflet blade less than 3" long 162

161a. Axillary buds easily visible, not covered by petiole; pith chambered: Flrs greenish, not showy; frt up to 2", more or less spherical nut—the commerical English walnut . . . . *Juglans regia*

161b. Axillary buds not visible, covered by petiole: Flrs white in pendulous clusters; frts flattened pods . . . . *Cladrastus kentuckea*

162a. Two to five yr old twigs dark green, spineless: Flrs yellowish/ white in long showy clusters; frt a pod . . . . *Sophora japonica*

162b. Two to five yr old twigs greyish brown, not dark green, stipular spines usually present 163

163a. Stems with abundant stiff hairs: Flrs rose-purple 164

163b. Stems not hairy: Flrs white except for a few cultivars; frt a flattened pod . . . . *Robinia pseudoacacia*

164a. Plants with fruits . . . . *Robinia fertilis*

164b. Fruits rare . . . . *Robinia hispida*

165a. Stems armed 166

165b. Stems unarmed 167

166a. Lvs once-pinnate, less than 1 foot long—Roses . . . . *Rosa*

166b. Lvs bi- or tripinnate, more than 2 feet long: Small white flrs borne in large umbel-like clusters; frts purplish-black berries . . . . . *Aralia spinosa*

167a. Lvs spiny: Flrs yellow; frts blue-black in grape-like clusters . . . . *Mahonia aquifolium*

167b. Lvs not spiny 168

168a. Some lflets lobed or deeply incised 169

168b. Lflets serrate/dentate 171

169a. Ground cover to 3 feet tall:
Flrs brownish purple,
before lvs . . . . *Xanthorhiza simplicissima*

169b. Trees or shrubs over 3 feet tall 170

170a. Shrub; lflets deeply incised and dissected giving a ferny appearance: Flrs greenish yellow, not showy, in dense clusters less than 8" long; frts crimson, not inflated . . . . *Rhus typhina* 'Dissecta'

170b. Trees; lflets merely incised:
Flrs yellow, showy, 12–15" open panicles; frts brown,
inflated . . . . *Koelreuteria paniculata*

171a. Lflets with 2–4 coarse teeth at base, otherwise entire: Flrs yellow/green in large clusters; frts winged and more visible than flrs . . . . *Ailanthus altissima*

171b. Lflets regularly toothed along margin 172

172a. None of lflets over 1 1/2" long:
Flrs greenish yellow;
frt a pod . . . *Gleditsia triacanthos* var. *inermis*

172b. Most lflets over 1 1/2" long 173

173a. Stem with chambered pith, walnut odor:
Frts more or less spherical, up to 2" diameter . . . 174

173b. Pith not chambered 175

174a. Lflets 5 to 9: Frt husk glabrous, shell thin—the commercial English walnut . . . . *Juglans regia*

174b. Lflets 11 to 23: Frt husk pubescent,
shell thick . . . . *Juglans nigra*

175a. Lflets up to 9—Hickory 176

175b. Lflets 9 or more 177

176a. Lvs 10–24"; 7 lflets (rarely 5 to 9) roughly equal size; marginal teeth tips hairless . . . . *Carya laciniosa*

176b. Lvs 8–14; 5 lflets (rarely 7) terminal lflets larger than basal ones; teeth tips hairy . . . . *Carya ovata*

177a. Some lvs with more than 20 lflets:
Flrs small greenish; frts in dense
dark red terminal clusters 178
177b. No lvs with more than 19 lflets 179

178a. Stems glabrous . . . . *Rhus glabra*
178b. Stems hairy . . . . *Rhus typhina*

179a. Lflets falcate; lvs exstipulate;
terminal buds yellowish: Frts in up
to 10" clusters, frt 1 1/2–3 1/2" long,
green to brown—Pecan . . . . *Carya illinoensis*
179b. Lflets not falcate; lvs stipulate;
terminal buds reddish brown: Frts in
clusters of 20 or more, frts 3/8" diameter
or less, orange red; flrs white, 1/3" across 180

180a. Lvs pinnately compound . . . *Sorbus aucuparia*
180b. Lvs simple . . . . *Sorbus aria*

181a. Lvs scale-like, about 1/8" long:
Flrs pink in elongate clusters . . . . *Tamarix*
181b. Lvs not scale-like, 1/4" or longer 182

182a. Ground cover or vines 183
182b. Trees or shrubs 195

183a. Ground cover, not vines 184
183b. Vine 188

184a. Lvs entire and up to 1 1/2" long:
Flrs white to pinkish, 1/4" or less;
borne in elongate nodding clusters 185
184b. Lvs toothed, 2–4" long: Flrs white
to pinkish but borne in erect spikes 187

185a. Lvs black dotted below, some lvs notched at
apex: Flrs bell-shaped; frt red berry 186
185b. Lvs not black dotted, revolute:
Flrs urn-shaped; frt red
fleshy drupe . . . . *Arctostaphylos urva-ursi*

186a. Shoots up to
1 foot high . . . . *Vaccinium vitis-idaea*
186b. Shoots up to 6" high; dense,
fine textured . . *Vaccinium vitis-idaea* 'Minus'

187a. Lvs up to 3" wide, gray to blue-green, often mottled above: Flr spikes borne at base of stem .... *Pachysandra procumbens*

187b. Lvs up to 1 1/2" wide, dark green above: Spikes borne at tip of stem .... *Pachysandra terminalis*

188a. Vines twining, no aerial roots or tendrils . . 191

188b. Vines clinging, with aerial roots or tendrils 189

189a. Tendrils wrapping around support: Attractive frts ranging from yellow to blue .... *Ampelopsis brevipedunculata*

189b. Tendrils not wrapping nor with aerial roots 190

190a. Tendrils with flattened adhesive disks at tip ...... *Parthenocissus tricuspidata*

190b. Tendrils none, clinging by aerial roots .... *Hedera helix*

191a. Lvs entire 192

191b. Lvs toothed 194

192a. At least young stems pubescent; petiole attached submarginally, petioles up to 6" long: Frts blue/black in clusters .... *Menispermum canadense*

192b. Stems glabrous; petioles attached at margin, petioles up to 3" long 193

193a. Lvs 4–10" long or longer: Flr U-shaped, 1–1 1/2" long; frts cylindrical .... *Aristolochia durior*

193b. Lvs up to 3 1/2" long (*P. boldschuanicum* very similar): Flrs small in groups of finger-like clusters; frts 3 angled .... *Polygonum aubertii*

194a. Pith lamellate: Frt elongate to 1 1/2" by 3/4" wide; seeds brown .... *Actinida arguta*

194b. Pith not lamellate, uniformly solid: Fruit spherical and about 1/3" diameter; seeds crimson/ orange .... *Celastrus scandens*

195a. Leaves entire 196
195b. Leaves toothed 277

196a. Stems armed 197
196b. Stems unarmed 202

197a. Petiole 1/2" or longer, lvs 2–5" long:
Fruit spherical, 3–5" diameter—
Hedgeapple . . . . *Maclura pomifera*
197b. Petiole less than 1/2" long: Frt less than 3/4" . . . 198

198a. Stems yellow beneath surface,
spines unbranched: Flrs yellow;
frt red . . . . *Berberis thunbergii*
198b. Stems not yellow 199

199a. Leaves and young stems with silvery
scales: Flrs 1–3 in leaf axils; frt red
or yellow 200
199b. Leaves green, without silvery scales:
Flrs many in conspicuous clusters;
frt orange/red, showy . . . . *Pyracantha coccinea*

200a. Lvs and branchlets with silvery
scales only, lvs up to 3" long:
Frt yellow . . . . *Elaeagnus angustifolia*
200b. Lvs with both brown and silvery
scales, lvs up to 4" long: Frt red 201

201a. Branchlets with both brown and silver
scales (speckled); pith brown:
Flrs in May/June . . . . *Elaeagnus umbellata*
201b. Branchlets with predominately brown
scales; pith greenish-white:
Flrs in fall . . . . *Elaeagnus pungens*

202a. Leaves heart-shaped: Flrs rosey
pink; frt a flattened pod . . . *Cercis canadensis*
202b. Leaves not heart-shaped: Frt not a pod . . 203

203a. Leaves with silvery
scales . . . . *Elaeagnus*—Go back to 200
203b. Leaves and young stems without
silvery scales 204

204a. Ocreae present: Small greenish-white flrs in finger-like clusters . . . . *Polygonum cuspidatum* var. *compactum*

204b. Ocreae absent 205

205a. Lf fan-shaped with parallel veins: Flrs none; seeds up to 1 1/2" long, yellowish orange, foul smelling . . . . . . *Ginkgo biloba*

205b. Lvs not fan-shaped 206

206a. Stipule scar encircling stem at nodes *OR* if circling stipule scars lacking, then flrs with a hypanthium and frts a cherry 207

206b. No scar encircling stem at nodes 219

207a. Lvs lobed, broadly truncate apex: Flr petals yellow with orange blotch within . . . . *Liriodendron tulipifera*

207b. Lvs unlobed, apex pointed 208

208a. Lvs a foot or more in length 209

208b. Lvs less than a foot in length 210

209a. Lvs cuneate at base, up to 2' long . . . . *Magnolia tripetala*

209b. Lvs subcordate or not tapered at base, to 3' long . . . . *Magnolia macrophylla*

210a. Lvs 5" or less long 211

210b. Some lvs 6" or more long 215

211a. Stipule scar encircling stem: Flrs 2" or > across, borne singly, petals more than 5; frts densely aggregated, opening to reveal red seeds 213

211b. Stipule scar small, not at all circling stem: Flrs < 1/2" across, 5 petals, white; frts blue/black cherries 212

212a. Glands on blade near junction with petiole: Flr clusters up to 5" long; sepal tips 3 toothed . . . . *Prunus laurocerasus*

212b. Glands on petiole: Flr clusters up to 3" long; sepal tips not toothed . . . . *Prunus caroliniana*

213a. Lvs smooth and shiny above, whitish below:
Flr buds narrow and sparingly pubescent;
often with some flrs through
September . . . . *Magnolia virginiana*

213b. Lvs somewhat crinkly/wavy and duller
above, lvs light green below, buds
plump, densely pubescent: Flrs restricted
to spring 214

214a. Lvs larger (3–5") and somewhat
obovate: Flr buds up to 1" long,
flrs with 12 tepals (6–15)
. . . . *Magnolia* × *loebneri*

214b. Lvs smaller (2–4") and less
obovate: Flr buds up to 5/8",
flrs with 12–18 tepals,
each 1 1/2–2" long,
straped shaped . . . . *Magnolia stellata*

215a. Stipule scar encircling stem:
Flrs 2" or > wide, petals > 5; frt not a cherry . . 216

215b. Stipule scar small, not at all
circling stem: Flr < 1" wide;
frt a cherry . . . . *Prunus laurocerasus*

216a. Lvs up to 10" long;
large tree at maturity:
Frts lumpy cucumber-like,
2–4" long . . . . *Magnolia acuminata*

216b. Lvs up to 7" 217

217a. Shrub to 12'; lvs 4–7" long:
Flrs with 6 tepals, purplish
outside . . . . (*M. quinquepeta*) *Magnolia liliflora*

217b. Trees to 30' (40'); lvs 3–6":
Flrs with 9 tepals 218

218a. Lvs 4–6" long: Flrs white,
late March-early
April . . . . . (*M. heptapeta*) *Magnolia denudata*

218b. Lvs 3–6" long; stems brown
with gray/white lenticels:
Flrs pink/purple on outside,
mid-late April . . . . . . *Magnolia* × *soulangiana*

219a. Lvs 6–12" long; buds naked, dark brown, pubescent: Flrs 1–2" across, purple; frts large banana-like . . . . *Asimina triloba*

219b. Lvs averaging smaller; buds scaled 220

220a. Aromatic when bruised or crushed, lvs dotted beneath 221

220b. Not aromatic, lvs not dotted 223

221a. Axillary buds superposed, upper ones clustered: Flrs small greenish-yellow; frts bright red . . . . *Lindera benzoin*

221b. Axillary buds solitary: Frts blue to grey 222

222a. Petioles 1/2" to 1 1/2" long; lvs lobed or unlobed: Frts 1/2", stalks scarlet . . . . *Sassafras albidum*

222b. Petioles shorter; lvs unlobed: Frts < 1/4", waxy, persistent through winter . . . . *Myrica pensylvanica*

223a. Trees 224

223b. Shrubs 247

224a. Cluster of buds at tip of stem: Frt an acorn—Oaks 225

224b. Buds not clustered 236

225a. Leaves unlobed and entire . . . . . . *Quercus imbricaria*

225b. Leaves lobed or toothed 226

226a. Lvs toothed or serrate with bristle tips . . . 227

226b. Lvs lobed 228

227a. Lvs finely toothed or serrate, bristle tipped . . . . *Quercus acutissima*

227b. Lvs coarsely toothed, mucronate teeth at most . . . . *Quercus muehlenbergii*

228a. Lobes with bristle tip 229

228b. Lobe tips without bristle 232

229a. Buds up to 1/2" long, pubescence buff or dirty gray, angled in cross section; lvs dark green, most lobes tend to widen above base . . . . *Quercus velutina*
229b. Buds smaller and reddish brown 230

230a. Buds broadly ovate with blunt tip, pale wooly pubesence in upper half . . . . *Quercus coccinea*
230b. Buds more narrow with sharper point, glabrous to lightly pubescent 231

231a. Terminal buds up to 1/4" long, more or less sharp pointed, glabrate; lvs usually with deeper sinuses, 5–7 lobes: Acorns up to 1/2" long . . . . *Quercus palustris*
231b. Terminal buds up to 1/2" long, sharp pointed, upper scales sometimes with rusty hairs; lvs usually not so deeply lobed, 7–11 lobes: Acorns up to 1" long . . . . *Quercus rubra*

232a. Some leaf bases auriculate (ear-like lobes): Acorns 1" long, elongate . . . . *Quercus robur*
232b. Lvs not auriculate 233

233a. Lvs glabrous or nearly so . . . . *Quercus alba*
233b. Lvs pubescent 234

234a. Lvs shallowly lobed; strap or needle-like appendages among terminal buds: Acorn cup not fringed . . . . *Quercus bicolor*
234b. Lvs deeply lobed 235

235a. Lf deeply lobed in lower half only; twigs pubescent: Acorn cup deep with dense fringe on rim . . . . *Quercus macrocarpa*
235b. Lvs with prominent lobe near middle (not deep sinus); twigs glabrous: Acorn with deep cup, not fringed . . . *Quercus lyrata*

236a. Lvs sessile to subsessile; smooth grey bark, sometimes exfoliating: Flrs vari-colored in large 6–8" clusters . . *Lagerstroemia indica*

236b. Leaves petioled 237

237a. Lvs averaging 3" or less in length 238

237b. Lvs usually more than 3" long 239

238a. Plants distinctly narrow upright: Frts 1/4", July on, red changing to purple-black; flrs yellowish-green and clustered in leaf axils, not showy . . . *Rhamnus frangula* 'Columnaris'

238b. Habit not columnar 240

239a. Lvs with 3 prominent veins from base on lower surface, some leaves asymmetrical at base; free of witches brooms: Frt 1/4", orange-red to purple, sweet, juicy . . . . *Celtis laevigata*

239b. Lvs not 3-veined, but pinnately veined; If base symmetrical 241

240a. Some lvs obovate, acute; buds naked; lvs deciduous: Frts purple/black at maturity . . . . *Rhamnus frangula*

240b. No lvs obovate, tips acuminate, lvs evergreen; buds scaled: Frts red on long pedicels . . . *Ilex pedunculosa*

241a. Some lvs clustered near stem tip: Flrs small, greenish-white in clusters; frts blue/purple and fleshy 242

241b. Lvs not clustered at tip 243

242a. Petioles 1–2" long; undersurfaces of lf appressed pubescent, lateral veins curved along lf margin, lvs ovate-elliptic: Flrs in terminal clusters, petals 4 . . . . *Cornus alternifolia*

242b. Petiole up to 1"; lower surface glabrous (some pubescence restricted to veins of young lvs); lvs elliptic-elongate: Flrs in axillary clusters, petals 5 . . . . *Nyssa sylvatica*

243a. Lvs long cuneate at base; lf scars prominent-raised; large shrub or small tree: White flrs borne in 6–8" fleecy panicles in spring . . . . *Chionanthus virginicus*

243b. Lvs not long cuneate 244

244a. Buds naked and hairy, lance-shaped, up to 1/4" long: Red berries ripening to black, 1/3" . . *Rhamnus caroliniana*

244b. Buds scaled 245

245a. Bud scales 2, overlapping: Flrs urn-shaped, creamy white, 1/2–3/4"; frts 1 1/2" diameter, pale orange—Persimmon . . . . *Diospyros virginiana*

245b. Bud scales 4 or more 246

246a. Petioles 1/2–1"; twigs slender, olive to bright red: White 1/4" urn-shaped flrs in 4–10" long drooping panicles; frts dry, 1/3" . . . . *Oxydendrum arboreum*

246b. Petioles 1/2–1 1/2"; twigs stout, buff or orange brown: Plants dioecious; fleshy frts borne in dense, globose 4–5" heads; flrs in subglobose heads or racemes . . . . *Maclura pomifera*

247a. Lvs averaging 2 1/2" or less 248

247b. Lvs larger 259

248a. Lvs ranging up to 1 1/4" long 249
248b. Lvs ranging up to 2 1/2" long 254

249a. Stipules absent: Flowers showy and fragrant, 6 or more flowers per umbel (usually terminal), stamens 8 250
249b. Stipules present, small, narrow: Flrs solitary or 2–3 per cluster along stem, stamens about 20; frt red 251

250a. Trailing/spreading, 6–12" high: Flrs rosey pink .... *Daphne cneorum*
250b. Upright to 4': Flrs white to pinkish tinged .... *Daphne × burkwoodii*

251a. Leaf margin undulating: Flrs pinkish, solitary, 1/4"; frts 1/4–3/8" . . *Cotoneaster apiculatus*
251b. Leaf margin not undulating 252

252a. Lvs up to 1/2"; low shrub, horizontal branches with laterals in flattened plane: Flrs pinkish, solitary or paired .... *Cotoneaster horizontalis*
252b. Some leaves up to 1 1/4" 253

253a. Habit prostrate with creeping stems, up to 1 1/2' high: Flrs white, solitary or in pairs .... *Cotoneaster dammeri*
253b. Habit upright/spreading, up to 6' high: Flrs pink, solitary or in three's .... *Cotoneaster divaricatus*

254a. Plants up to 6" high; low, dense evergreen ground cover: Flrs pinkish, axillary, nodding, corolla 4-parted; frt red, 1/2–3/4" .... *Vaccinium macrocarpon*
254b. Plants larger and erect 255

255a. Twigs angled to squarish with wings: Flrs varicolored in large 6–8" clusters .... *Lagerstroemia indica*
255b. Twigs and infloresence not as above 256

256a. Twigs green: Flrs unisexual,
small, greenish-white; frts black
1/4" drupe . . . . *Ilex glabra*

256b. Twigs not green: Flrs bisexual;
frts red or black 257

257a. Lvs with small stipules; bark not exfoliating 258

257b. Lvs without stipules; bark exfoliating:
Flrs white, 1/4", axillary or in
terminal clusters; frt black . . . . *Vaccinium arboreum*

258a. Petioles 1/4 to 1/2":
Flrs white in showy clusters;
frt red . . . . *Cotoneaster multiflorus*

258b. Petioles less than 1/4":
Flrs pinkish white,
not showy; frt black . . . . *Cotoneaster lucidus*

259a. Buds naked or with 2 scales 260

259b. Buds imbricate with more than 2 scales 263

260a. Buds naked: Flrs in leaf axils,
creamy, parts in 5's, not showy;
frt 1/4" drupe, red changing to black 261

260b. Buds scales 2: Flrs in large
terminal clusters 262

261a. Habit distinctly narrow
upright . . . . *Rhamnus frangula* 'Columnaris'

261b. Habit not columnar . . . . *Rhamnus frangula*

262a. Lvs up to 1 1/2" wide,
lvs glabrous below: Flrs up to
1" across, 5 parted, very showy;
frt a 5 valved capsule . . . . . . *Kalmia latifolia*

262b. Lvs up to 2 1/2" wide,
lvs appressed pubescent below:
Individual flrs < 1/4", 4 parted,
not showy; frt a drupe . . . . *Cornus alternifolia*

263a. Lvs wrinkled/rugose above with impressed
veins: Flrs in 2" wooly clusters,
malorderous; frts red . . . . . . *Cotoneaster salicifolius*

263b. Lvs not as above 264

264a. Buds clustered at tip of stems, central flr bud larger than surrounding vegetative buds: Large clusters of showy flrs—Rhododendrons . . 265
264b. Buds not as above and not dimorphic . . . 269

265a. Lvs rusty-scaly beneath; evergreen 266
265b. Lvs not rusty-scaly beneath 267

266a. Lvs with yellow glandular dots . . . . *Rhododendron* 'P.J.M.'
266b. Lvs not as above . . . . *Rhododendron carolinianum*

267a. Lvs glabrous (both sides); evergreen . . . . *Rhododendron catawbiense*
267b. Lvs with at least some pubescence; deciduous . . 268

268a. Lvs pubescent on both surfaces: Flrs well before the lvs . . . . *Rhododendron mucronulatum*
268b. Lvs pubescent on veins beneath at maturity . . . *Rhododendron schlippenbachii*

269a. Pith chambered: Flrs golden yellow and before lvs, 3/4" or more long 270
269b. Pith solid: Flrs white or if yellow, 1/8" long 271

270a. Stem green: Flrs pale yellow, least showy of the Forsythias . . . . *Forsythia europaea*
270b. Stem gray/brown: Flrs bright yellow . . . . *Forsythia ovata*

271a. Pith green: Flrs white to pink, urn-shaped, 1/3", axillary racemes in May; frt blue-black berry . . . *Vaccinium corymbosum*
271b. Pith white or off-white, or yellow-orange/brown 272

272a. Pith tan or orange brown: Large (6–10") open, highly branched inflorescence, flrs and frts small and sparce 273
272b. Pith white or off-white: Flrs conspicuous rather than the inflorescence 274

273a. Pith yellow-orange/brown; lvs up to 3 1/4" long (several purple leaved cultivars); lf scars not lobed ..... *Cotinus coggygria*

273b. Pith tan; lvs up to 6" long; lobed lf scars .... *Cotinus obovatus*

274a. Deciduous, up to 30': Flrs white 275

274b. Evergreen, up to 4': Flrs rosy-purple, strong fragrance; frt a drupe .... *Daphne odora*

275a. Lvs mucronate/apiculate: Flrs 5 petaled, odorless; frt a 5 lobed capsule .... *Exochorda racemosa*

275b. Lvs not as above: 4 linear petals, fragrant; mature frts dark blue 276

276a. Lvs oblongish (3–8"), not conspicuously leathery: Flrs on previous year's wood .... *Chionanthus virginicus*

276b. Lvs smaller, roundish, leathery: Flrs on current year's growth .... *Chionanthus retusus*

277a. Lvs fan-shaped with parallel veins: Flrs none; frts (seeds) up to 1 1/2" long, yellowish orange, foul odor .... *Ginkgo biloba*

277b. Lvs not as above; flowering plants 278

278a. Lvs mostly crowded at end of branches: Flrs creamy yellow to orange with red veins in pendulous clusters; frt a capsule ...... *Enkianthus campanulatus*

278b. Lvs not crowded 279

279a. Stems armed 280

279b. Stems unarmed 291

280a. Lvs 7–14" wide, palmately lobed: Flrs small, white, in 12–24" clusters; frt a small black drupe 281

280b. Lvs less than 5" wide: Inflorescences much smaller 282

281a. Lvs 5–7 lobed, sinuses shallow . . . *Kalopanax pictus*

281b. Lobes prominent, sinuses reaching to 2/3 the base . . . . *Kalopanax pictus* var. *maximowiczii*

282a. Stipules conspicuous, broad rounded and foliar: Flrs 1 1/2" across, orange-red (ranging from white to scarlet); frts up to 2 1/2", fleshy, yellowish green 283

282b. Stipules absent or not as above: Flrs white (creamy-green) 284

283a. Habit upright to 6–10'; stipules up to 1 1/2" wide . . . *Chaenomeles speciosa*

283b. Habit spreading up to 3'; stipules up to 3/4" wide . . . *Chaenomeles japonicum*

284a. Spines short, borne at stem tip, not laterally: Flrs greenish yellow, 4-petaled; frt 1/4", black . . . . *Rhamnus cathartica*

284b. Spines lateral along branches: Flrs not 4-petaled; frt not black 285

285a. Lvs borne along spines: Flrs small, white in 2" clusters; frts orange-red in showy clusters . . . . *Pyracantha coccinea*

285b. Spines leafless 286

286a. Trees; stout spines 1–3" long: Flrs white, 5-parted—Hawthorns 287

286b. Shrubs; spines less than 1" long, some 3-pronged: Flrs yellow, 6-parted; frt red, rare . . . . *Berberis* × *mentorensis*

287a. Lf base truncate or subcordate; lvs shallowly to distinctly lobed 288

287b. Lf base cuneate 289

288a. Thorns slender to 3" long; lvs distinctly 3–5 lobed, veins extending to sinuses and to lobe tips: Styles 4–5; frts 1/3" or less . . . . *Crataegus phaenopyrum*

288b. Thorns stout to 2" long; lvs shallowly 7–10 lobed, veins extending to lobe tips only: Styles 2–5; frts 1/2" or more . . . . . *Crataegus mollis*

289a. Lvs glabrous; thorns 1 1/2–3" long: Stamens 10 . . . . *Crataegus crusgalli*

289b. Lvs with some pubescence below; thorns up to 1 1/2": Stamens 20 290

290a. Lvs pubescent beneath, lvs unlobed: Styles 1–3, inflorescence hairy; frts > 1/2" . . . . *Crataegus* × *lavallei*

290b. Pubescence restricted to vein axils below, lvs shallowly lobed near tip: Styles 2–5; inflorescence glabrous; frts < 1/2" . . . . . *Crataegus viridis*

291a. Many lvs 3(5)-lobed 292

291b. Lvs not as above 301

292a. Lvs distinctly white (tomentose) below: Catkins 2–3" long, before lvs . . . *Populus alba*

292b. Lvs not white below 293

293a. Trees 294

293b. Shrubs 296

294a. Sinuses rounded (U or C-shaped): Flrs and frts not bract borne; frts juicy—Mulberry 295

294b. Sinuses not rounded (V-shaped): Flrs and frts on leaf-like bract; frt not juicy . . . . *Tilia mongolica*

295a. Lvs smooth above, pubesence (if any) restricted to veins below . . . . *Morus alba*

295b. Lvs usually rough above, pubesence not restricted to veins below . . . . *Morus rubra*

296a. Lobes in upper half of lvs near apex 297
296b. Lobes not restricted to upper half 298

297a. Teeth not restricted to upper half; apex acuminate: Flrs double, up to 1 1/2" wide; no frts . . . *Prunus triloba* var. *multiplex*
297b. Teeth restricted to upper half; apex not acuminate: Flrs 1/2" wide; frts dry . . . . *Spiraea* × *vanhouttei*

298a. Stipules present: Flrs not yellow; frts not juicy 299
298b. Stipules absent: Flrs greenish-yellow to yellow; frts juicy 300

299a. Bark not peeling in strips; buds inconspicuous: Flrs 2" or more across . . . . *Hibiscus syriacus*
299b. Bark peeling on young and old stems; buds easily visible: Flrs < 1/2" across in 1–2" clusters . . . . *Physocarpus opulifolius*

300a. Petioles about 1/2" long; young branches glabrous: Flr clusters erect; frt scarlet . . . . *Ribes alpinum*
300b. Some petioles 1" or more long; young branches pubescent: Flr clusters nodding, fragrant; frts black or yellow . . . . *Ribes odoratum*

301a. Buds stalked 302
301b. Buds not stalked 311

302a. Catkins present all year: Seed catkins woody and cone-like 303
302b. No catkins 304

303a. Lf tip blunt, lvs roundish . . . . *Alnus glutinosa*
303b. Lf tip pointed . . . . *Alnus incana*

304a. Bark exfoliating on old branches: Flrs with showy crimson stamens . . . . *Parrotia persica*
304b. Bark not exfoliating: Stamens not crimson 305

305a. Buds with 2 oppositely place scales, one overarching the other at tip: Flrs (April–May) consisting of white to cream colored stamens in 1–2" bottle-brush terminal spikes, no petals 306

305b. Bud scales (if present) not overarching: Flrs in Jan.–March or Oct.–Nov.; flrs with 4 narrow, crumpled yellow or red petals—Witchhazels 307

306a. Two to 4' tall; lvs up to 2 1/2" long . . . . *Fothergilla gardenii*

306b. Six to ten feet tall; lvs up to 4" long . . . . *Fothergilla major*

307a. Lvs pubescent on one or both surfaces 308

307b. Mature lvs glabrous except sometimes on veins below 309

308a. Lvs pubescent above and grayish tomentose beneath . . . . . . *Hamamelis mollis*

308b. Lvs lightly pubescent below, lvs more narrow than *H. mollis* . . . . *Hamamelis × intermedia*

309a. Some lvs up to 6" long: Flowering in November . . . . . . *Hamamelis virginiana*

309b. Lvs up to 5" long: Flowering January–March . . . 310

310a. Lvs obovate, 4–6 vein pairs: Petals 1/2" long . . . . *Hamamelis vernalis*

310b. Lvs ovate, 5–8 vein pairs: Petals 3/4" long . . . . *Hamamelis japonica*

311a. Lvs orbicular, suborbicular to heart-shaped 312

311b. Lvs not as above 322

312a. Lvs subopposite and borne on short spurs: Dioecious; flrs in leaf axils, male flrs with many stamens, female flrs with 3–6 pistils/styles; frt a 3/4" pod . . . . . *Cercidiphyllum japonicum*

312b. Lvs distinctly alternate, not on spurs: Frts not pods 313

313a. Petiole flattened: Flrs in catkins . . *Populus tremuloides*
313b. Petiole not flattened: No catkins 314

314a. Bud scales 5–7 with pale margin; trees with showy flr display 315
314b. Bud scales 2–3, buds lopsided: Flrs and frts borne on leaf-like bract—Lindens 316

315a. Lvs dentate-serrate; petioles 1 1/2–3" long: Flr clusters subtended by 2 large (up to 7") white bracts; frts 1 1/2" drupe . . *Davidia involucrata*
315b. Lvs crenate; petioles up to 1 1/2" long: Flrs with 5 white petals; frts 1/2" or less . . . . *Pyrus calleryana* 'Bradford'

316a. Lf surface glabrous below 317
316b. Lvs pubescent below 319

317a. Lvs 4–8" long; hairs in axils of lateral veins but not basal veins . . . . *Tilia americana*
317b. Lvs up to 4" long; all vein axils with tufts of hairs 318

318a. Twigs and buds greenish-yellow below, light reddish brown above . . *Tilia × euchlora*
318b. Twigs brown above and below; buds uniformly brown or light greenish-yellow . . . . *Tilia cordata*

319a. Petiole glabrous (See Dirr on the status of this species) . . . . *Tilia heterophylla*
319b. Petiole pubescent 320

320a. Underside of lvs lightly pubescent with axillary tufts of hairs . . . . *Tilia platyphyllos*
320b. Underside of lvs white tomentose without axillary tufts of hairs 321

321a. Branches ascending . . . . *Tilia tomentosa*
321b. Branches pendulous . . . . *Tilia petiolaris*

322a. Lvs with spiny teeth or lobes: Flrs in axillary clusters, small, whitish; frts red—Holly 323
322b. Lvs not spiny 327

323a. Lvs rectangular with 3 pointed lobes at end: Flrs on previous years growth . . . . *Ilex cornuta*
323b. Lvs not as above (more regularly toothed) 324

324a. Lf with undulating margin 325
324b. Lvs planar, not undulating 326

325a. Lvs up to 3" long: Flrs on previous yrs growth . . . . *Ilex aquifolium*
325b. Lvs up to 4–5" long . . . . *Ilex × altaclarensis*

326a. Lvs dull green above, remotely toothed; up to 50′ tall: Flrs on current growth . . . . *Ilex opaca*
326b. Lvs glossy, teeth more closely set; up to 15′ tall . . . . *Ilex × meserve*

327a. Lvs with 2–4 glands on petiole near blade junction *OR* glands somewhere on blade only *OR* glands distributed over petiole and blade . . . 328
327b. Lvs not glandular 354

328a. Glands on petiole/blade junction: Ovary superior, fleshy drupe; 1 style 334
328b. Glands on petiole and blade *OR* blade only 329

329a. Small dot-like glands distributed on petiole and blade 349
329b. Glands on blade only: Petals 5, flrs borne in clusters, usually showy; frts fleshy or juicy 330

330a. Dark glands on midrib: Ovary inferior, pome; styles 5 331
330b. Glands on teeth or serrations: Ovary superior, fleshy drupe; 1 style 332

331a. Lvs glabrous below: Inflorescence glabrous or nearly so; frts black . . . . *Aronia melanocarpa*

331b. Lvs pubescent to tomentose below: Inflorescence pubescent; frts red . . . . *Aronia arbutifolia*

332a. Shrub 4–5′ tall; lvs 3/4–1" wide; linear stipules: Flrs double or single . . . . *Prunus glandulosa*

332b. Trees; lvs wider 333

333a. Lvs gland-dotted below; bark strikingly handsome red-brown: Flrs white in 2–3" racemes; frts 1/4", red turning black . . . . *Prunus maackii*

333b. Glands on teeth; bark pale gray; habit rounded to spreading, 40–50′: Flrs in clusters of 2–6, flowering before lvs (sometimes with lvs) . . . . *Prunus* × *yedoensis*

334a. Lvs purple when mature 335

334b. Lvs not purple 336

335a. Terminal bud present; lvs up to 5" long; habit pyramidal, dense; lvs green at first: Flrs many in long racemes . . . . *Prunus virginiana* 'Schubert'

335b. Terminal bud absent; lvs up to 2 1/2" long: Flrs in clumps of 3 or less; flrs before lvs, highly fragrant . . . . *Prunus cerasifera*

336a. Some lvs more than 4 1/2" long 337

336b. Lvs 4 1/2" or less 342

337a. Lvs dull, some obovate; veins compressed; lvs out early: Flrs in drooping 3–8" racemes . . . . *Prunus padus*

337b. Lvs shiny 338

338a. Lvs remotely toothed to entire; evergreen, large shrub: Flrs in 3–5" racemes, highly fragrant . . . . *Prunus laurocerasus*

338b. Lvs serrate or serrulate 339

339a. Lvs long and narrow (up to 1 1/2" wide); tip long acuminate; lvs and stem glabrous: Flrs borne singly, sessile, before lvs—Peach . . . . *Prunus persica*

339b. Lvs broader 340

340a. Lvs broad elliptic-obovate, rounded or subcordate at base; bark dark reddish brown with prominent lenticels: Flrs in 2–6 sessile clusters, single, 1 1/2" across or more . . . . *Prunus sargentii*

340b. Lvs more narrow, ovate-oblong or ovate-lanceolate 341

341a. Lf serrations incurved, without bristles, thickened: Flrs in drooping 4–6" racemes—Common Black Cherry . . . . *Prunus serotina*

341b. Lf serrations with bristle tips: Flrs in 3–5 clusters along stems before or with lvs . . . . *Prunus serrulata*

342a. Lvs up to 2 1/2" long 343

342b. Lvs more than 2 1/2" long 344

343a. Twigs warty; lvs pubescent on both sides; long acuminate: Flrs double . . . . *Prunus* 'Hally Jolivette'

343b. Twigs not warty; lvs glabrous above, short pointed: Flrs usually solitary and not double . . . . *Prunus cerasifera*

344a. Lvs with some pubescence 345

344b. Lvs glabrous 347

345a. Petiole 1/2" to 1" long; bark black with prominent lenticels: Flrs in clusters of 3–4; pedicels red . . . . *Prunus nigra*

345b. Petioles 1/4" or less 346

346a. Lvs glabrous above, pubescent on veins below; weeping forms: Frts black at maturity . . . . . *Prunus subhirtella*

346b. Lvs densely pubescent above and below and on twigs; habit spreading; densely twiggy shrub; exfoliating: Early flowering; frts red . . . *Prunus tomentosa*

347a. Petioles short, less than 1/4": Flrs 1–3, nearly sessile; frts pubescent . . . . *Prunus tenella*

347b. Petioles about 1/2" or longer 348

348a. Twigs reddish: Flrs white . . . . *Prunus pensylvanica*

348b. Twigs not reddish: Flrs red to deep rose . . . *Prunus campanulata*

349a. Bark white: Flrs in catkins—Birches 350

349b. Bark not white 388

350a. Lf tips long acuminate 351

350b. Lf tips not long acuminate 353

351a. Most lvs shouldered and distinctly long acuminate: Male catkins 2–3 1/2" long and borne singly at end of branches . . . *Betula populifolia*

351b. Most lvs not shouldered (hence triangular) 352

352a. Lvs 3/4–1 1/2" wide, glabrous, petiole 3/4" or <: Male catkins mostly in 2's along stem, wing of nutlet twice as wide as nutlet and wide spreading . . . *Betula pendula*

352b. Lvs generally wider, glabrous or with axillary tufts of hairs below, petiole 3/4" or >: Male catkins predominantly borne singly at end of branches, wing of nutlet not as wide as *B. pendula* and ascending slightly . . . . *Betula platyphylla* var. *japonica*
It is not clear that this entity is distinct from *B. populifolia*.

353a. Some lvs rounded at base;
veins pubescent below:
Lobes of catkin bracts ascending . . . *Betula papyrifera*

353b. Lvs wedge shaped or truncate at base;
glabrous below: Lobes of bracts
divergent . . . . *Betula pendula*

354a. Trees 355

354b. Shrubs 418

355a. Lvs lobed 356

355b. Lvs not lobed 367

356a. Buds clustered at tip of stem:
Frts acorns . . . . . . *Quercus*—Go back to 225

356b. Buds not clustered: Frts not acorns 357

357a. Base of petiole enclosing bud;
bark exfoliating revealing large
patches of white to greenish cream color 358

357b. Buds not enclosed by petiole;
bark not as above 359

358a. Lvs more pubescent than *P.* × *acerifolia;*
lobes of lf broader than long:
Frt clusters spherical,
borne mostly singly . . . . *Platanus occidentalis*

358b. Lf lobes about as long as broad:
Frt clusters mostly
in 2's . . . . *Platanus* × *acerifolia*

359a. Lvs conspicuously lobed, palmately veined 360

359b. Lvs not as above 362

360a. Lf star shaped with nearly
equal lobes, pointed: Frts dry
in spherical clusters . . *Liquidambar styraciflua*

360b. Lvs irregularly lobed; lobe tips
usually rounded, sometimes pointed:
Frts juicy in clusters, reddish-
purple at maturity—Mulberry 361

361a. Lvs usually smooth above, glabrous below
or with some pubesence on veins . . . . . . *Morus alba*

361b. Lvs often scabrous above,
pubescent surface below . . . . *Morus rubra*

362a. Bark white or cinnamon-brown and profusely exfoliating except on very young trees: Flrs in catkins; frts tiny, winged—Birches 364

362b. Bark not as above: Flrs not in catkins, in showy clusters; frts small pomes—Hawthorns 363

363a. Lf base cordate; twigs (2nd yr) ridged/rough; no thorns: Male flrs in catkins; frts surrounded by stiff foliose husk . . . . *Corylus colurna*

363b. Lvs not cordate; twigs not ridged, often with thorns: Flrs not in catkins, in showy clusters; frts small pomes—Hawthorns 365

364a. Bark white; lvs deeply incised with pointed tips . . . *Betula pendula* var. *crispa* . . . . or 'Dalecarlica'

364b. Bark cinnamon brown and profusely exfoliating; lvs shallowly lobed or unlobed . . . . *Betula nigra*

365a. Lvs obovate and cuneate at base (more toothed and less obovate than the species): 10 stamens, anthers red . . . . *Crataegus crusgalli* var. *inermis*

365b. Lvs not obovate: Stamens 20, anthers yellow . . . 366

366a. Buds and leaves glabrous (except vein axils): Flr clusters 2" across; 2–5 styles . . . . *Crataegus viridis*

366b. Buds and lvs densely pubescent: Flr clusters 3–4" across; 4–5 styles . . . . *Crataegus mollis*

Note: There are a few *Malus* forms (Crab-apples) that have somewhat lobed leaves. *Malus* can be distinguished from *Crataegus* on the basis of fruits. *Crataegus* frts (carpels) are bony when ripe. *Malus* carpels are not bony when ripe; they may be papery or leathery.

367a. Buds clustered at tip of stem:
Frts acorns . . . . *Quercus*—Go back to 225
367b. Buds not clustered: Frts not acorns 368

368a. Buds covered with a single scale (wraps around bud), usually long and rather narrow: Male and female catkins on separate plants 369
368b. Buds not as above (with more than one scale) 375

369a. Lvs much longer than wide, usually lanceolate . . 370
369b. Lvs about half as wide as long, ovate to oval, variable, rugose above: Flrs in large soft silky catkins in early spring before lvs (often confused with *S. discolor*) . . . . *Salix caprea*

370a. Lvs glabrous (at maturity) 371
370b. Lvs silky 374

371a. Lvs linear-lanceolate 373
371b. Lvs oblanceolate (narrow but wider above middle); some lvs opposite; buds and catkins purplish 372

372a. Shrub 8–10'(18') tall; lvs 2–4" long, green . . . . *Salix purpurea*
372b. Compact shrub to 5' tall; lvs smaller and blue green . . . . *Salix purpurea* 'Nana'

373a. Branches contorted . . . . *Salix matsudana* 'Tortuosa'
373b. Branches not contorted . . . . *Salix matsudana*

374a. Weeping; branches yellow (the typical weeping willow) . . . *Salix alba* 'Tristis'
374b. Upright; branches ascending, yellow-green . . . . *Salix alba*

375a. Lvs cuneate at base: Flrs white 376
375b. Lvs not cuneate 377

376a. Lvs 4–6" long: Flrs 3" across; frts a 5-valved capsule . . *Franklinia alatamaha*

376b. Lvs 1 1/2–3" long: Flrs small, inconspicuous; frts a berry-like drupe, scarlet to red (some cultivars yellow) . . . . *Ilex decidua*

377a. Bark smooth, grey 379

377b. Bark not smooth nor grey: Catkins 378

378a. Lf base cordate; twigs ridged: Frts in a stiff foliose husk, frt a large unwinged nut . . . . *Corylus colurna*

378b. Lvs not cordate; twigs not ridged: Frts not enclosed, frt a small winged nut . . . . *Betula*—Go back to 349

379a. Buds 3/4–1" long; lvs slender with sharp point: Nuts covered with a spiny husk—Beeches 380

379b. Buds shorter 381

380a. Lvs up to 5" long; 9–15 vein pairs; margin coarsely serrate . . . . *Fagus grandifolia*

380b. Lvs up to 4" long; 5–9 vein pairs; margin entire or nearly so . . . . *Fagus sylvatica*

381a. Bud scales 10 or more in 4 rows; stipule scars present; false terminal bud 383

381b. Bud scale < 8 and not in 4 rows; stipule scars absent; true terminal bud 382

382a. Lvs up to 4" long: Flrs and frt in a flat-topped cluster . . . *Sorbus alnifolia*

382b. Lvs up to 3" long: Flrs and frts in elongate clusters—Serviceberry . . . 384

383a. Buds appressed and curving around stem; buds 1/4–1/2" long, brown: Bracts of pistilate catkins up to 1 1/2" long . . *Carpinus betulus*

383b. Buds not curling around stem; buds 1/4" or less, dark brown to black: Bracts about 1" long . . . . *Carpinus caroliniana*

384a. Lvs with teeth restricted to upper half or nearly so 385
384b. Lvs toothed to the base or nearly so 386

385a. Lvs up to 2 1/2" long: Petals up to 1/3" long; racemes to 1 1/2" long ...... *Amelanchier alnifolia*
385b. Lvs up to 1 1/2" long: Petals up to 5/8" long; racemes to 3" long .... *Amelanchier florida*

386a. Young lvs glabrous or nearly so, purplish when young: Racemes glabrous .... *Amelanchier laevis*
386b. Young lvs pubescent; pith green: Racemes tomentose 387

387a. Lvs up to 2 1/2" long; apex usually rounded; base rarely cordate: Sepals erect or spreading; petals 1/3" long .... *Amelanchier canadensis*
387b. Lvs up to 3 (4)" long; apex usually acute or acuminate; base usually cordate: Sepals reflexed; petals 1/8" long .... *Amelanchier arborea*

388a. Lvs triangular; petiole flattened: Infloresence a catkin 389
388b. Lvs not as above 390

389a. Terminal buds 3/8" long; narrow habit with ascending branches ..... *Populus nigra* 'Italica'
389b. Terminal buds 1/2–3/4" long; spreading branches .... *Populus deltoides*

390a. Branches contorted/twisted corkscrew-like: Frts red, juicy—Mulberry .... *Morus australis*
390b. Branches not contorted 391

391a. Leaf terminating stem a short distance beyond axillary bud (leaving short peg at leaf fall); rubbery sap when leaf or twig torn; pith chambered: Flrs inconspicuous; frts winged, flattened, notched at apex .... *Eucommia ulmoides*
391b. Not as above 392

392a. Lvs up to 1 1/2(2) inches long, 1/4–3/4" wide; stems whitish-grey: Dioecious, small greenish-white flrs; frts red in axillary clusters . . . . *Ilex vomitoria*

392b. Lvs larger 393

393a. Bud scales 3 or less 394

393b. Bud scales 4 or more 395

394a. Lvs finely serrulate; petiole winged or flanged: Flrs showy, white, 2–4" across; frts woody dehiscent capsule . . . . *Stewartia ovata*

394b. Lvs coarsely serrate or toothed and sharp pointed; petiole not winged: Flrs inconspicuous in catkins; frts in a large spiny husk . . . . *Castanea mollissima*

395a. Bark on 3–5" stems exfoliating freely, cinnamon brown: Flrs and frts in catkins . . . . *Betula nigra*

395b. Not as above 396

396a. All buds 1/2" long, woolly, grey to grey-brown: Numerous white flrs creating showy display in spring before lvs; frts brown, 1/2" or less . . . . . *Pyrus calleryana* 'Bradford'

396b. Buds less than 1/2' and not woolly 397

397a. Pith chambered 398

397b. Pith not chambered 400

398a. Bark or trunks and older limbs with corky ridges or warty; 2nd year twigs not stringy: Flrs inconspicuous; frts small unwinged drupes—Hackberry 399

398b. Bark not corky or warty; bark stringy on 2nd year twigs: Flrs white, bell-shaped; frts 4-winged . . . . *Halesia carolina*

399a. Lf margin consistently serrate; lf tip acute to acuminate; bark rough in corky ridges; buds up to 1/4" long . . . . *Celtis occidentalis*

399b. Lf margin entire or sometimes with a few teeth; long acuminate; bark merely warty; buds smaller: Frts sweet . . . . *Celtis laevigata*

400a. Strong odor when twigs bruised or crushed 401

400b. Twigs lacking strong odor 402

401a. Twigs with wintergreen odor; lvs mostly cordate: Reproducing by catkins . . . . *Betula lenta*

401b. Bruised twig odor not wintergreen; lvs rarely cordate: No catkins . . . . *Prunus*—Go back to 332

402a. Bark shreddy, separating in longitudinal strips which are free at each end; lf margin with sharp teeth of various sizes, doubly serrate, softly pubescent: Reproducing by catkins, male catkins usually in 3's and about 1" long, female catkins much larger with bladder-like segments . . . . . *Ostrya virginiana*

402b. Plants not as above 403

403a. Some lvs exceeding 6" long 404

403b. Lvs not exceeding 6" 406

404a. Lvs cuneate, oblong, margins serrulate or entire: Showy flr display; flrs 1/4" urn-shaped, white in 4–10" clusters; frts 5-valved capsules . . . . *Oxydendrum arboreum*

404b. Lvs rounded ovate, truncate or subcordate at base, conspicuously toothed or serrate: Frts 1/2–1", purple at maturity, delicious—Mulberry . . 405

405a. Lvs usually smooth above, glabrous below or with some pubescence on veins . . . . *Morus alba*

405b. Lvs often scabrous above, pubescent surface below . . . . *Morus rubra*

406a. Petioles 3/4" or less in length 410

406b. Some petioles 3/4" or more in length 407

407a. Upper surface of lvs glossy and smooth 408

407b. Upper surface not glossy nor smooth 409

408a. Petioles up to 1" long; buds up to 1/4" and pointed: Flrs not showy, stamens 4; frts a mulberry . . . . *Morus alba*

408b. Petioles up to 1 1/2" long; buds smaller and rounded: Flrs showy, white, stamens 20; frts small red pomes . . . . . . *Crataegus viridis*

409a. Lvs up to 5 or more inches long: Flrs and frts as in 408a . . . . *Morus rubra*

409b. Lvs up to 3 1/2" long: Flrs and frts as in 408b . . . . *Crataegus mollis*

410a. Lvs with 3 veins arising from base; tips long acuminate: Flrs inconspicuous; frts small drupe . . . . *Celtis laevigata*

410b. Lvs not 3-veined, lateral veins arising regularly and pinnately along the midvein 411

411a. Lvs 2-ranked (rows) on stems:
Flrs small, not showy, without
petals; frts samara or drupe 412

411b. Lvs spirally arranged on stem:
Flrs with petals, showy 1/2" or more;
frt a pome 417

412a. Lvs simply serrate 413

412b. Lvs doubly serrate; buds often
not centered over leaf scar 415

413a. Buds sharp-pointed and divergent;
veins ending in teeth tips and
forming slight projection:
Frt a small drupe . . . . *Zelkova serrata*

413b. Buds globular, blunt, often not
centered over leaf scar; lvs less
than 3" long: Frts samaras with circling wing . . . 414

414a. Buds small, 1/8" or less:
Flrs and frts in fall . . . . *Ulmus parvifolia*

414b. Buds larger, 1/4", dark with
hairs along edge of scales:
Flrs and frts in spring . . . . *Ulmus pumila*

415a. Lvs up to 6" long:
Samara margin hairy . . . . *Ulmus americana*

415b. Lvs up to 4" long:
Samara margin smooth 416

416a. Petioles 1/8 to 1/4" long;
buds 1/4" long; young branchlets
pubescent: Seed centrally located
in samara . . . . *Ulmus glabra*

416b. Petioles 1/4 to 1/2" long;
buds 1/8" long; young branchlets
glabrous or nearly so: Seed apically
positioned in samara . . . . . *Ulmus carpinifolia*

417a. Lateral veins straight to margin, regularly & pinnately arranged along midvein; upper surface glabrous: Flrs and frts in 2–3" flat-topped clusters . . . . *Sorbus alnifolia*

417b. Lateral veins curving; upper surface usually pubescent: Flrs and frts not as above . . . . *Malus*

418a. Lvs distinctly lobed 419

418b. Lvs not lobed 422

419a. Lvs linear, some lvs at least 4" long 420

419b. Lvs not linear 421

420a. Lf margin irregular: Flrs perfect, not in catkins; frts berry-like, red to black . . . . . . *Rhamnus frangula* 'Asplenifolia'

420b. Lvs regularly lobed: Flrs staminate or pistilate, in catkins; frts a brown nutlet . . . . *Comptonia peregrina*

421a. Lobes restricted to upper half of leaf; leaf base cuneate: Very showy in flower, white . . . . *Spiraea* × *vanhouttei*

421b. Lvs lobed to base; truncate at base: Not showy in flr . . . . *Stephanandra incisa*

422a. Lvs with conspicuous orbicular stipules: Flrs 1 1/2" or less in diameter, orange/red, before lvs 423

422b. Stipules (if present) not as above: Flrs not as above 424

423a. Habit upright to 6–10 feet; stipules up to 1 1/2" wide . . . *Chaenomeles speciosa*

423b. Habit spreading up to 3'; stipules up to 3/4" wide . . . . *Chaenomeles japonica*

424a. Stems winged, brilliant pink to red fall color: Flrs yellow/green, inconspicuous; frts opening to reveal orange/red seeds (In the common cultivar 'Compactus', the wings often much reduced) . . . . . . *Euonymus alatus*

424b. Stems not winged: Flrs not as above 425

425a. Lvs intensely reddish purple: Flrs white(pinkish); frts purple/black . . . . *Prunus × cistena*

425b. Lvs not red/purple 426

426a. Most lvs 3/4" or less in width 427

426b. Most lvs wider than 3/4" 437

427a. Stem green at least on current yrs growth: Frts black 1/4" drupe 428

427b. Stems not green 429

428a. Lvs with small teeth near apex; stems green for 2–3 yrs: Flrs 5–8 merous . . . . *Ilex glabra*

428b. Lvs serrulate; stems green only on current year: Flrs 4 merous . . *Ilex crenata*

429a. Lvs 3/4" or < long, 1/3" or less wide: Flrs urn-shaped, pinkish, small; frt red . . . . *Vaccinium macrocarpon*

429b. Lvs larger; not ground covers 430

430a. Lvs 1/4" or < wide (1–1 1/2" long): Small white flrs in umbels, early spring before lvs . . . . *Spiraea thunbergii*

430b. Lvs wider 431

431a. Lvs 2" or less long 432

431b. Some lvs 2" or more long 434

432a. Stems whitish grey (purplish initially): Dioecious, greenish-white, axillary clusters; translucent scarlet drupes . . . . *Ilex vomitoria*

432b. Stems orange/reddish brown: Flrs perfect, showy in flower; frts dry brown follicles 433

433a. Lvs pubescent beneath; narrowly obovate, up to 1/2" wide: Flrs double, white, before lvs . . . . *Spiraea prunifolia*

433b. Lvs glabrous beneath, lvs up to 3/4" wide; not obovate: Flrs white, with lvs . . . . *Spiraea nipponica* 'Snowmound'

434a. Lvs pubescent below at least on midvein 435

434b. Lvs glabrous 436

435a. Lvs usually with obtuse apex; stems grayish: Frts orange/red, pit rough . . . . *Ilex decidua*

435b. Lvs acute or acuminate; stems olive brown to purplish brown: Frt red, pit smooth . . . . *Ilex verticillata*

436a. Lvs obtuse or slightly pointed; caducous stipules; 2–5' high bush: Flrs 1/2–3/4" across, pink to white, not urn-shaped, axillary; frt a drupe . . . . *Prunus tenella*

436b. Lvs acute/pointed; no stipules; 9–12' upright shrub with stiff spreading branches: Flrs small (1/3"), white, urn-shaped, borne in terminal 3–6" long drooping racemes; frt a capsule . . . . *Pieris japonica*

437a. Stems 3 or more yrs old are distinctly and uniformily green; 3–6' shrub: Flrs yellow, 5 petals . . . . *Kerria japonica*

437b. Stems not green except occasionally on current growth 438

438a. Trunks and larger stems with smooth light grey bark 439

438b. Larger stems (trunk size rarely obtained) not with smooth grey bark 440

439a. Lvs 5–6" long, gradually narrowed at base: Flrs white, solitary, 3" across, petals broad; frt a capsule .... *Franklinia alatamaha*

439b. Lvs 3 1/2" or less long, base not tapered: Flrs smaller, white, racemes, petals narrow; frt a pome .... *Amelanchier*—Go back to 381

440a. Lvs distinctly aromatic when bruised, resin dotted: Flrs unisexual, perianth absent; frt small whitish, waxy, persistent .... *Myrica pensylvanica*

440b. Lvs not aromatic or resin dotted 441

441a. Pith chambered 442

441b. Pith not chambered 444

442a. Lvs pubescent on veins below: Flrs white; frt red .... *Ilex verticillata*

442b. Lvs glabrous: Flrs yellow; frt brownish capsule 443

443a. Young stems green; petioles up to 1/3" long: Flrs up to 1" wide, singly or 2–3 together .... *Forsythia europaea*

443b. Young stems grey-brown; petioles up to 1/2" long: Flrs up to 3/4" wide, mostly solitary .... *Forsythia ovata*

444a. Lvs lanceolate, 2–5" long by 1 1/2" wide, long acuminate: Flrs small, white in 2–3" long racemes .... *Leucothoe fontanesiana*

444b. Lvs not lanceolate, not long acuminate . . 445

445a. Twigs pubescent 446

445b. Twigs glabrous or nearly so 450

446a. Twigs glandular-pubescent: Flrs unisexual in dimorphic catkins, not showy—Hazelnut, Filbert ... 447

446b. Twigs pubescent but not glandular: Flrs bisexual, showy, white or pink 449

447a. Lvs 2 1/2 to 6" long, 1 1/2–2 1/2" wide: Outer covering twice as long as nut . . . . *Corylus americana*

447b. Lvs 2–4" long by 1 1/2 to 3" wide: Outer covering about as long as nut 448

448a. Branches contorted . . . . *Corylus avellana* 'Contorta'

448b. Branches not contorted . . . . *Corylus avellana*

449a. Lvs up to 4" long, some obovate; petiole 1/8–3/4" long: Flrs in 2–6" cylindrical clusters . . . . *Clethra alnifolia*

449b. Lvs up to 3" long, lvs not obovate; petioles about 1/8" long: Flrs in flat-topped clusters . . . . *Spiraea japonica*

450a. Pith solid, green: Flrs small, white to pink, urn-shaped; blue/black berry . . . . *Vaccinium corymbosum*

450b. Pith not green: Flrs not urn-shaped 451

451a. Twigs roughened by lenticels and longitudinal fissures: Flrs white, 1 1/2" wide, in 3–5" racemes . . . *Exochorda racemosa*

451b. Twigs not roughened 452

452a. Twigs zig-zagged; petioles winged or flanged; buds solitary or superposed, elongate: Flrs white, 3" wide, solitary, axillary . . . *Stewartia ovata*

452b. Twigs, petioles and buds not as above: Flrs smaller, clustered 453

453a. Lvs stipulate, often falling early and often thread-like: Flrs usually with 1 pistil; frt a drupe, fleshy . . . *Prunus*—Go back to 332

453b. Exstipulate: Flrs usually with 5 pistils; frt a dry follicle 454

454a. Lvs rhombic-ovate; teeth restricted to upper half of leaf; twigs rounded: Flrs borne along arching stems, very showy in flr, always white . . . . *Spiraea × vanhouttei*

454b. Lvs not as above; twigs angular: Flrs borne in flat-topped clusters above the foliage, flrs white to red 455

455a. Lvs reddish-bronze when young; twigs with slight ridges; habit up to 4′ tall, finer and more dense than *S. japonica* . . . . *Spiraea × bumalda*

455b. Lvs not as above; twigs angular but not ridged; 4–5′ tall . . . . *Spiraea japonica*

KEY TO GYMNOSPERMS

1a. Lvs broad, fan-shaped, parallel veins: Dioecious; cones absent, pollen produced in 1" long catkin-like structures; seeds stalked, borne singley, fleshy, green to yellow-orange, foul odor when crushed . . . . *Ginkgo biloba*

1b. Lvs and reproductive structures not as above: Cones present (sometimes highly modified) 2

- 2a. Most lvs whorled **OR** in clusters **AND** 1" or more long: Cones woody with overlapping scales 3
- 2b. Lvs not **BOTH** clustered **AND** not 1" or more long: Cones woody or fleshy 21

3a. Lvs in clusters of 5 or less: Cone scales bearing 2 seeds 4

3b. Lvs in whorls or clusters of 10 or more: Scales with 2 or more seeds 17

- 4a. Lvs in clusters of 3 or mostly 3's; bark exfoliating creating irregular brownish to whitish patches: Cones sessile, 2–3" long, 2" across, yellowish brown, recurved spine at tip of scale . . . . *Pinus bungeana*
- 4b. Lvs in clusters of 2 or 5 5

5a. Lvs in 2's 6

5b. Lvs in 5's 12

- 6a. Lvs mostly 3" or less long 7
- 6b. Lvs mostly longer than 3" 9

7a. Current year stems reddish purple with a light colored bloom (glaucous); not common in nursery trade: Cones nearly sessile, up to 3" long by 1 1/2" wide, dark reddish brown; prickle present at tip of each scale . . . . *Pinus virginiana*

7b. Young stems not purple, not glaucous 8

8a. Lvs bluish green; bark of upper branches and trunk orange; usually a tree with single trunk: Cones to 3" long, grey-brown, prickle minute . . . . *Pinus sylvestris*

8b. Lvs dark green; bark not orange; often compact, bushy and multistemmed: Cones nearly sessile, up to 2" long; scale tip with dark ring, no prickle . . . . *Pinus mugo*

9a. Young stems green with whitish bloom (glaucous); buds pubescent and not resinous; bark reddish to orange on upper branches and trunk; habit often asymmetrical: Cones short stalked, to 2" long, 1" broad, tawny yellow, small prickle or absent . . . . *Pinus densiflora*

9b. Young stems not glaucous; bark of upper trunk and branches not orange 10

10a. Buds not resinous; lvs 2 1/2–4 1/2" long: Cones short stalked and to 3" long, prickle small or absent, cones brown . . . . *Pinus thunbergiana*

10b. Buds resinous; lvs longer (up to 5–6") 11

11a. Lvs stiff and ending in horny point, dull, do not break when bent: Cones nearly sessile, to 3 1/2" long; scales transversely keeled, usually with prickle . . . . *Pinus nigra*

11b. Lvs sharp pointed but flexible, shiny, snap when bent . . . . *Pinus resinosa*

12a. Lvs 5–8" long: Cones with 1–2" stalk, up to 10" long by 2" wide, resinous . . . . *Pinus wallichiana*
12b. Lvs 5" or less 13

13a. Lvs 1 3/4" or less: Cones nearly sessile, to 4" long, prickles 1/4" and curved . . . *Pinus aristata*
13b. Lvs longer 14

14a. Lf edges smooth to touch; young stems shiny green and extremely flexible (according to Dirr, can be tied in knots): Cones short stalked, to 6" long (10"), resinous . . . . *Pinus flexilis*
14b. Lf edges minutely toothed 15

15a. Lvs soft and flexible; stems with tufts of short hairs subtending leaf clusters: Cones stalked, to 8" long, often curved, pendent, prickles present . . . . *Pinus strobus*
15b. Lvs rather stiff; stem pubescence not as above . . . 16

16a. Pubescence on 1 yr stems dense, orange-brown: Cones short stalked, to 3" long, cones never open . . . . *Pinus cembra*
16b. Pubescence sparse to glabrous: Cones nearly sessile; to 4" long; scales few and leathery/ woody . . . . *Pinus parviflora*

17a. Lvs 2–5" long: Cones to 4" long, scales with reflexed margins, each scale with 5–9 narrow winged seeds . . . . *Sciadopitys verticillata*
17b. Lvs 2 1/2" or less: Cone scales with 2 seeds 18

18a. Lvs 1 1/2" or less in length 19
18b. Lvs up to 2 1/2" long: Cone scales deciduous; cone 2–3" long . . . . *Pseudolarix kaempferi*

19a. Lvs stiff: Cone scales deciduous; cone 3–5" long . . . . *Cedrus libani*
19b. Lvs not stiff: Cone scales persistent; cones less than 2" long 20

20a. Lvs with two conspicuous white bands below; lvs on spur shoots, 40 or more: Cone scales reflexed at apex . . . . *Larix kaempferi*

20b. Lvs with inconspicuous white bands below; 30–40 lvs on spur shoots: Cone scale apex not reflexed . . . . *Larix decidua*

21a. Lvs whorled: Cones to 3" long by 2" wide, upright on upper sides of branches; scales dropping at maturity . . . . *Cedrus atlantica* ('Glauca' and 'Glauca Pendula' are common cultivars.)

21b. Lvs not whorled 22

22a. Lvs linear, distinct, more or less perpendicular to stem 23

22b. Lvs scale-like or awl-like, overlapping and hugging the stem 44

23a. Lvs angular (in cross section): Cones pendulous, scales not dropping 24

23b. Lvs flat (two sided) 29

24a. Branchlets reddish to orange brown (particularly on vigorous growth); terminal branches conspicuously pendulous; lvs dark green: Cones cylindrical to 6" long, scale edges finely toothed . . . . *Picea abies*

24b. Branchlets not as above 25

25a. Stems of branches pubescent; lvs less than 1/2" long: Cones 3 1/2" long, scale edges entire . . . . *Picea orientalis*

25b. Stems glabrous; lvs longer: Cones to 2 1/2" by 3/4", scales suborbicular, margins nearly entire 26

26a. Lvs stout, stiff and prickly, up to 1 1/2" long: Cones to 4"; scale margins wavy, toothed at apex 28

26b. Lvs not prickly, lvs up to 3/4" long, disagreeable odor when bruised . . . *Picea glauca* (for cultivars see couplet 27)

27a. Dense dwarf form, appears to be
sheared—Dwarf Alberta Spruce . . *Picea glauca* 'Conica'
27b. Compact, slow growing—
Black Hills Spruce . . . . *Picea glauca* 'Densata'

28a. Lvs bluish green . . . . *Picea pungens* var. *glauca*
28b. Lf color variable but
not distinctly blue . . . . *Picea pungens*

29a. Terminal buds sharp pointed, smooth,
shiny, 1/4 to 1/3" long: Cones not
erect, 3 pronged exerted bracts
subtending scales . . . . *Pseudotsuga menziesii*
29b. Terminal buds not sharp pointed,
buds smaller: Cones erect or not 30

30a. Lf scars conspicuous and circular
and not protruding from stem:
Cones erect, scales deciduous
leaving persistent central axis 31
30b. Lf scars not as above: Cones not erect 37

31a. Buds resinous 33
31b. Buds not resinous: Cones reddish brown 32

32a. Lvs nearly parallel to stem;
bud scales free at tips hence
buds rough: Cones to 10" long,
bracts hidden . . . . *Abies cilicica*
32b. Lvs more widely spreading; bud
scale tips appressed: Cones to
6" long, bracts exerted . . . *Abies nordmanniana*

33a. Lvs 1 1/2" or longer, glaucous
bluish green: Cones to 6" long,
bracts hidden . . . . *Abies concolor*
33b. Lvs up to about 1" long, dark green:
Cones to 4" long 34

34a. Twigs brown or reddish brown:
Cones to 2 1/2" long 35
34b. Twigs (2 yrs) grey 36

35a. Young twigs grey with short reddish pubescence: Bracts much exerted ..... *Abies fraseri*
35b. Young twigs brown, short pubescence not reddish: Bracts slightly exerted ...... *Abies veitchii*

36a. Young twigs brown: Bracts slightly exerted .... *Abies veitchii*
36b. Young twigs grey (with soft grey hairs): Bracts hidden ..... *Abies balsamea*

37a. Lvs with two white lines above or below 38
37b. Lvs without white lines 40

38a. Lvs with white lines above: Cones to 2 1/2" long, scale margins finely toothed .... *Picea omorika*
38b. Lvs with white lines below: Cones to 1 1/2" long, scale margins entire 39

39a. Lf margins entire: Cones to 1 1/2" long by 1" wide, scales pubescent .... *Tsuga caroliniana*
39b. Lf margins finely toothed (use hand lens): Cones to 1" by 1/2" wide, scales glabrous .... *Tsuga canadensis*

40a. Lvs up to 2mm wide, lvs sessile: Cones globular, green to brown, about 1" diameter 43
40b. Lvs 2–4mm wide, lvs with short petiole: Seeds ovoid, 1/4" diameter with a fleshy red cover (aril) 41

41a. Lf tips acuminate .... *Taxus baccata*
41b. Lf tips abruptly short pointed 42

42a. Two to three yr old branches reddish brown; buds scales acute .... *Taxus cuspidata*
42b. Two yr old branches olive green; bud scales obtuse .... *Taxus × media*

43a. Lvs and branchlets opposite; buds conspicuous on secondary branches: Cones with long stalks . . . *Metasequoia glyptostroboides*

43b. Lvs and branchlets alternate; buds inconspicuous . . . . *Taxodium distichum*

44a. Lvs alternate, i.e. spirally arranged: Cones globular to 1" diameter; scales with toothed or spiny tips, each scale with 3–5 seeds . . . . *Cryptomeria japonica*

44b. Lvs opposite or in threes 45

45a. Branchlets arranged in flattened sprays 56

45b. Branchlets not flattened: Cones (1/3") berry-like due to fleshy scales, bluish, gin odor 46

46a. Lvs all awl shaped 47

46b. Lvs mostly scale-like but with some awl-shaped lvs 51

47a. Crushed twigs and lvs emit disagreeable odor: Cones on recurved stalks . . . . *Juniperus sabina* var. *tamariscifolia*

47b. Odor not disagreeable 48

48a. Lvs decurrent: Cones with 1 seed or with 3 seeds 49

48b. Lvs not decurrent: Staminate cones axillary, cones with 3 seeds 50

49a. Lvs with 2 white dots and lines near base of lf below or on edge: Cones with 3 seeds . . . . *Juniperus procumbens* (*J. procumbens* is often treated as a variety of *J. chinensis*)

49b. Lvs dotless and without white lines below, upper surface with 2 greyish-white bands: Cones with 1 seed . . . . . . *Juniperus squamata*

50a. Lvs spreading at wide angle from the stem, lvs concave above but not grooved: Seeds without longitudinal grooves on back .... *Juniperus communis*

50b. Lvs overlapping, deeply grooved above: Seeds without longitudinal grooves .... *Juniperus conferta*

51a. Virtually all lvs opposite 52

51b. Ternate lf arrangement frequently found among awl-shaped lvs 55

52a. Strong odor from crushed twigs and lvs: Cones on recurved stalk 53

52b. Odor not strong: Cones with 2 seeds, seeds triangular .... *Juniperus scopularum*

53a. Unpleasant odor when crushed; generally more erect and bushy than the following 54

53b. Pleasant odor, mat-like appearence due to trailing branches .... *Juniperus horizontalis* ('Wiltonii' the Blue Rug juniper is a popular cultivar)

54a. Lvs mostly awl-shaped; low spreading/mounded; less odor than the species .... *Juniperus sabina* var. *tamariscifolia*

54b. Lvs mostly scale-like; generally more erect and bushy; often used as a ground cover .... *Juniperus sabina*

55a. Awl lvs mostly opposite, up to 1/4" long, no whitish bands above: Cones bluish .... *Juniperus virginiana*

55b. Awl lvs mostly ternate (at least more common than those above), 1/3" or longer, 2 whitish bands on upper surface: Cones brown at maturity .... *Juniperus chinensis*

56a. Some lvs with long tapering points 57
56b. Lf tips shorter and blunter 59

57a. Lvs with whitish lines below: Cones woody at maturity, with more than 4 scales 58
57b. Lvs without whitish lines below; plants 1–2′ tall and spreading: Cone scales 4 . . . . *Microbiota decussata*

58a. Lvs long pointed throughout: Cones globose, scales peltate, not overlapping . . . . . . *Chamaecyparis pisifera*
58b. Long pointed leaves on vigorous shoots only: Cones cylindric/ ovoid, scales not peltate, scales overlapping . . . . *Thuja plicata*

59a. Lvs with white lines below: Cone scales peltate 60
59b. Lvs without white lines below: Cone scales peltate or imbricate 61

60a. Lvs blunt, glands (on outer surface) minute: Pollen cones yellow, seeds narrowly winged . . *Chamaecyparis obtusa*
60b. Lvs acute, glands (on outer surface) large: Pollen cones crimson, seeds broadly winged . . . . *Chamaecyparis lawsoniana*

61a. Branches drooping: Cones globose, scales peltate, not overlapping . . . . *Chamaecyparis nootkatensis*
61b. Branches not drooping (except *Thuja occidentalis* 'Pendula'): Cones cylindric/ovoid, scales not peltate, scales overlapping 62

62a. Sprays held vertically; often multiple trunks: Cones with 6–8 scales, without prickles; seeds wingless . . . *Thuja (Platycladus) orientalis*

62b. Sprays oriented horizontally; usually one trunk: Cones with 8–10 scales each with curved prickle; seeds with narrow wing . . . . *Thuja occidentalis*

GLOSSARY

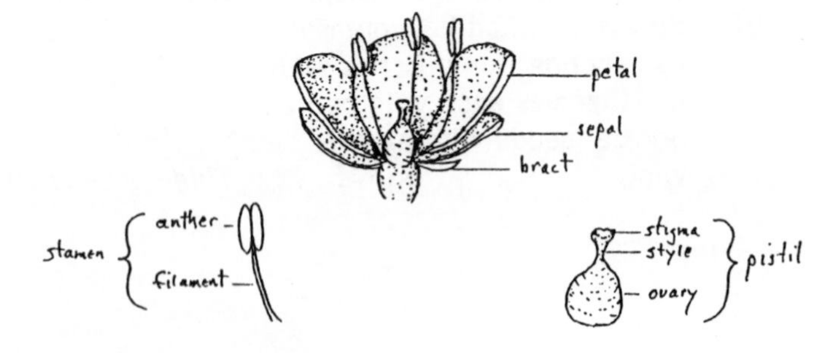
petal
sepal
bract
stamen
anther
filament
stigma
style
ovary
pistil

Figure 1: Parts of an idealized flower

Acuminate: apex tapering to a point.

Acute: a non-tapering apex that approaches a right angle.

Anther: the pollen-bearing part of a flower/stamen (see Figure 1).

Apiculate: a short pointed tip.

Armed: bearing prickles, spines, thorns.

Awl-like: tapering from base to a pointed apex.

Axil: the angle between leaf and stem on the upper side.

Axillary: located in the axil.

Axillary bud: bud located in an axil.

Berry: a fleshy fruit without a hard pit.

Bipinnate: a leaf with 2 orders of branching.

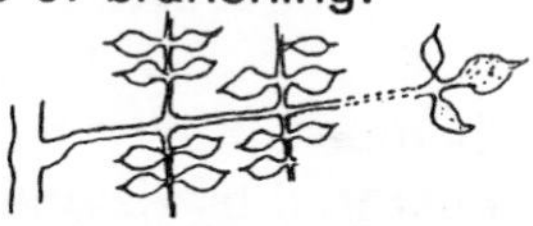

Bisexual: flrs having both stamens and pistils.

Blade: the expanded, flattened portion of a leaf.

Bracts: a leaf-like structure subtending a flr (see figure 1) or flr cluster (inflorescence).

Bud: an undeveloped branch or flr cluster with or without scales.

Bud scale: outer covering structures of a bud.

Bundle scar: a mark within a leaf scar that represents the severed end of a vascular bundle.

Caducous: falling away early.

Calyx: collective term for the sepals.

Calyx tube: a tube-like structure formed by fused sepals.

Capsule: a dry fruit splitting open into two or more sections.

Carpels: a unit or section of a compound pistil; simple pistils have only one carpel.

Catkin: a spike-like inflorescence composed of small non-showy flrs more or less covered by scales. Willows, birches, cottonwood, etc.

Chambered pith: pith with horizontal diaphragms separated by cavities.

Compound leaf: a leaf divided into two or more sections (leaflets)

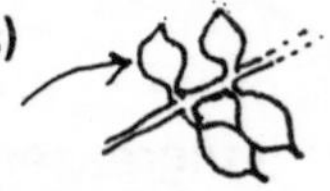

Cone scale: individual units of a gymnosperm seed cone bearing seeds (ovules) on the upper surface.

Connate: fusion of parts.

Cordate: heart-shaped.

Corolla: collective term for petals.

Crenate: leaf margin with rounded teeth.

Cuneate: tapering or wedge-shaped, normally referring to a leaf base.

Deciduous: annual dropping of leaves.

Decurrent: extending down the stem.

Decussate: organs in alternating pairs, each pair at right angles to adjacent pairs resulting in 4 rows.

Dehiscent: splitting open to allow escape of enclosed units.

Dentate: margin with sharp pointed teeth directed outward.

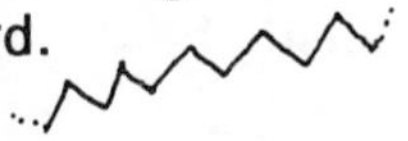

Denticulate: small or finely dentate.

Dimorphic: having two shapes or forms.

Dioecious: having pistillate and staminate flrs on separate plants.

Doubly serrate: having a small serration on a larger one.

Drupe: fleshy fruit with a hard, stony pit.

Entire: smooth margin.

Exfoliating: bark peeling away.

Exstipulate: without stipules.

Falcate: sickle-shaped.

Filament: the stalk portion of a stamen (see figure 1).

Foliose: leaf-like.

Follicle: a dry fruit opening along one side.

Glabrate: nearly glabrous.

Glabrous: without pubescence (hairs, etc).

Glaucous: a whitened surface substance that is easily rubbed off.

Hispid: surface with stiff or bristly hairs.

Husk: an outer covering.

Hypanthium: a cup or saucer shaped structure from which sepals, petals and stamens project.

Imbricate: overlapping like shingles on a roof.

Imperfect flower: flrs with stamens or pistils but not both.

Incised: If blade irregularly cut or divided.

Inferior ovary: flr parts arising above the ovary.

Inflorescence: a cluster of flrs; there are various terms for different arrangements or branching patterns such as catkin, panicle, raceme, umbel.

Internode: portion of stem between the nodes (see node).

Keeled: with a ridge, as on the bottom of a boat.

Lamellate pith: a solid pith with horizontal diaphragms.

Lamellate: having plates, septa or lamellae.

Lanceolate: long narrow, widest below middle, tapering to a point.

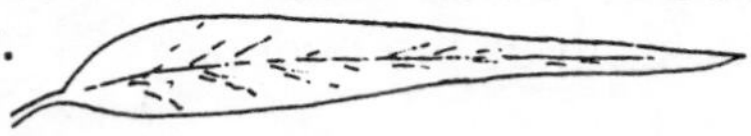

Lateral bud: buds along the sides of a stem, non-terminal.

Leaf scar: scar left at site of former leaf attachment.

Leaflets: blade-like portions of a compound leaf: (See compound leaf)

Lenticels: elongate (usually) pustule-like areas on the surface of woody plants.

Merous: numbers of parts, as in 3-merous; meaning having 3 petals, 3 stamens, etc.

Mucronate: a broad apex abruptly terminated by a short point or tip.

Naked buds: buds without bud scales.

Node: Point of attachment of lvs on the stem.

Nut: Fruit with a hard wall, sometimes covered with a husk (walnut, hickory nut) or only partially covered as in *Corylus* and oak acorns.

Nutlet: a small nut.

Obovate: Egg-shaped with the broadest portion above the middle.

Obtuse: blunt or rounded tip.

Ocreae: a thin sheathing structure (collar) around the stem at the nodes.

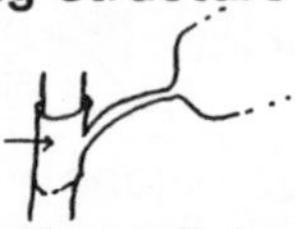

Orbicular: circular in outline, disk-shaped.

Ovate: egg-shaped with the broader portion below the middle.

Palmate: radiating from a common point; refers to leaflets in a compound leaf or veins from the base of a lf.

Panicle: a type of inflorescence that is highly branched.

Pedicel: stalk of each flr in an inflorescence.

Peltate: supporting stalk is centrally attached.

Perfect flower: a flr with both pistils and stamens.

Petiole: narrow stalk (usually) of a leaf.

Pilose: covered with dense soft hairs.

Pinnate: lflets or veins arranged along a central axis.

Pith: the center non-woody tissue of a stem or twig.

Pome: a fleshy fruit with a central core as in an apple.

Pubescent: presence of hairs or hair-like structures on plant surfaces.

Raceme: a type of inflorescence with an unbranched central axis bearing stalked flrs along the axis.

Rachis: an axis bearing lateral branches, leaflets, or flrs.

Revolute: margin (edge) of leaf rolled toward the lower surface.

Rugose: surface appearing coarsely wrinkled.

Samara: a winged fruit as in maple or elm.

Scabrous: rough to the touch.

Scale-like: a small leaf usually appressed to the stem and usually with a rounded tip (not gradually tapering).

Serrate: teeth along margin are saw-like with tips directed toward the tip.

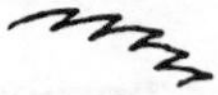

Serrulate: with small serrations.

Sessile: without a stalk or petiole.

Shell: hard covering, beneath the husk, enclosing the edible portion of a nut.

Shouldered leaf: with an abrupt transition from wide base to narrow tip.

Shrub: multistemmed woody plant not reaching tree-like proportions.

Simple leaf: a leaf with a single undivided blade, without leaflets.

Sinus: the space separating lobes of a lobed leaf.

Spike: a type of inflorescence with sessile flrs borne along an unbranched axis, as in wheat.

Spur shoot: a short, condensed lateral branch.

Stellate: hairs with radiating laterals appearing star-like.

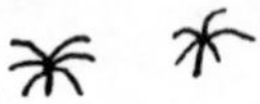

Stipular spines: a stiff, rigid stipule, appearing as a thorn or spine.

Style: a slender portion of a pistil between the stigma and ovary. (see figure 1)

Superior ovary: an ovary positioned above the other flr parts as in figure 1.

Superposed: one placed above another.

Tendril: a curved lateral appendage used to grasp other structures for support.

Tepal: perianth parts not assignable to sepals or petals, as in tulips or magnolias.

Terminal bud: the bud at the tip of a stem.

Ternate: in threes.

Tomentose: covered with dense soft woolly hairs.

Toothed: a general term for projections along a margin separated by notches.

Tree: usually a single stemmed (trunk) woody plant obtaining large size.

Trifoliate: with three leaflets.

Tripinnate: leaf with three orders of branching (see bipinnate).

Truncate: blunt, as if cut off. or

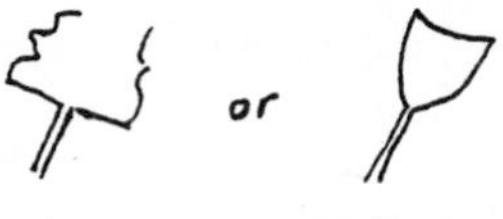

Umbel: a type of flat-topped inflorescence with pedicels arising from the same point.

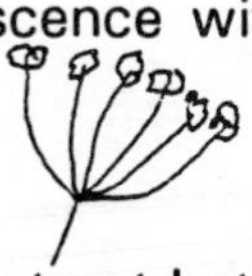

Unisexual: having stamens or pistils but not both.

Valvate: bud scales that meet along their edges but do not overlap.

Vascular bundle scar: places or marks in a leaf scar where vascular bundle was severed at leaf fall (see leaf scar).

Vegetative bud: buds that produce stems and leaves rather than flowers. Usually smaller than flower buds.

Villose: long soft non-matted hairs.

SCIENTIFIC NAME INDEX

The number preceding the scientific name is the page number on which it can be found.

The number(s) following the scientific name refer to the couplet number.

G preceding a couplet number indicates gymnosperm key

Number without prefix indicates angiosperm key

71	*Abies balsamea,* G36b.	Balsam Fir
70	*Abies cilicica,* G32a.	Cilician Fir
70	*Abies concolor,* G33a.	Concolor Fir, White Fir
71	*Abies fraseri,* G35a.	Fraser Fir
70	*Abies nordmanniana,* G32b.	Nordmann Fir
71	*Abies veitchii,* G35b., G36a.	Veitch Fir
25	*Acanthopanax sieboldianus,* 149a.	Fiveleaf Aralia
8	*Acer buergeranum,* 19a.	Trident Maple
9	*Acer campestre,* 26b.	Hedge Maple
10	*Acer × freemanii,* 32b.	Freeman Maple
8	*Acer ginnala,* 22a.	Amur Maple
12	*Acer griseum,* 46a.	Paperbark Maple
9	*Acer japonicum,* 28b.	Fullmoon Maple
9	*Acer miyabei,* 26a.	Miyabe Maple
12	*Acer negundo,* 50a.	Boxelder, Ash-leaved Maple
9	*Acer nigrum,* 30a.	Black Maple
9, 13	*Acer palmatum,* 28a., 55a.	Japanese Maple
8	*Acer pensylvanicum,* 20a.	Striped Maple, Moosewood, Whistlewood
9	*Acer platanoides,* 25b.	Norway Maple
10	*Acer pseudoplatanus,* 31a.	Planetree Maple, Sycamore Maple
8, 10	*Acer rubrum,* 20b., 32b.	Red Maple
10	*Acer saccharinum,* 32a.	Silver Maple, Soft Maple
9	*Acer saccharum,* 30b.	Sugar Maple, Hard Maple
8, 12	*Acer tataricum,* 22b., 43b.	Tatarian Maple
9	*Acer truncatum,* 25a.	Purpleblow Maple, Shantung Maple

30	*Actinidia arguta,* 194a.	Bower Actinidia, Tara Vine
14	*Aesculus flava (octandra),* 60b.	Yellow Buckeye
14	*Aesculus glabra,* 60a.	Ohio Buckeye, Fetid Buckeye
13	*Aesculus hippocastanum,* 57a.	Common or European Horsechestnut
14	*Aesculus parviflora,* 58a.	Bottlebrush Buckeye
14	*Aesculus pavia,* 59a.	Red Buckeye
13	*Aesculus* × *carnea,* 57b.	Red Horsechestnut
28	*Ailanthus altissima,* 171a.	Tree of Heaven
25	*Akebia quinata,* 150b.	Fiveleaf Akebia
44	*Alnus glutinosa,* 303a.	Common, Black or European Alder
44	*Alnus incana,* 303b.	White, Speckled or Gray Alder
63	*Amelanchier,* 439b.	
55	*Amelanchier alnifolia,* 385a.	Saskatoon Serviceberry
55	*Amelanchier arborea,* 387b.	Downy Serviceberry, Juneberry, Shadbush, Servicetree, Sarvis-tree
55	*Amelanchier canadensis,* 387a.	Shadblow Serviceberry
55	*Amelanchier florida,* 385b.	Pacific Serviceberry
55	*Amelanchier laevis,* 386a.	Alleghany Serviceberry
30	*Ampelopsis brevipedunculata,* 189a.	Porcelain Ampelopsis
27	*Aralia spinosa,* 166b.	Devils-walkingstick, Hercules-club
29	*Arctostaphylos uva-ursi,* 185b.	Bearberry, Kinnikinick
30	*Aristolochia durior,* 193a.	Dutchman's Pipe
48	*Aronia arbutifolia,* 331b.	Red Chokeberry
48	*Aronia melanocarpa,* 331a.	Black Chokeberry
34	*Asimina triloba,* 219a.	Common Pawpaw
42	*Berberis* × *mentorensis,* 286b.	Mentor Barberry
31	*Berberis thunbergii,* 198a.	Japanese Barberry
54	*Betula,* 378b.	Birch
57	*Betula lenta,* 401a.	Sweet, Black or Cherry Birch
52, 56	*Betula nigra,* 364b., 395a.	River or Red Birch
51	*Betula papyrifera,* 353a.	Paper, Canoe or White Birch

50, 51	*Betula pendula,* 352a., 353b.	European White Birch
52	*Betula pendula* var. crispa, 364a.	
52	*Betula pendula* 'Dalecarlica', 364a.	
50	*Betula platyphylla* var. japonica, 352b.	Asian White Birch
50	*Betula populifolia,* 351a.	Gray Birch
14	*Buddleia davidii,* 63a.	Butterfly-bush, Summer Lilac
20	*Buxus microphylla,* 109a.	Boxwood, Littleleaf Box or Boxwood
20	*Buxus sempervirens,* 109b.	Boxwood, Common Box or Boxwood
7	*Calluna vulgaris,* 8a.	Scotch Heather
20	*Calycanthus floridus,* 110a.	Common Sweetshrub, Carolina Allspice
13	*Campsis radicans,* 54a.	Trumpetcreeper, Trumpet Vine
25	*Caragana arborescens,* 152a.	Siberian Peashrub
54	*Carpinus betulus,* 383a.	European Hornbeam
54	*Carpinus caroliniana,* 383b.	American Hornbeam, Blue Beech Ironwood, Muscle-wood, Water Beech
29	*Carya illinoensis,* 179a.	Pecan
28	*Carya laciniosa,* 176a.	Shellbark Hickory
28	*Carya ovata,* 176b.	Shagbark Hickory
56	*Castanea mollissima,* 394b.	Chinese Chestnut
10	*Catalpa,* 35b.	
6	*Catalpa bignioides,* 5b.	Southern Catalpa
6	*Catalpa speciosa,* 5a.	Northern Catalpa
69	*Cedrus atlantica,* G21a.	Atlas Cedar
69	*Cedrus atlantica* 'Glauca', G21a.	
69	*Cedrus atlantica* 'Glauca Pendula', G21a.	
68	*Cedrus libani,* G19a.	Cedar of Lebanon
30	*Celastrus scandens,* 194b.	American Bittersweet
36, 57, 58	*Celtis laevigata,* 239a., 399b., 410a.	Sugar Hackberry, Sugarberry
57	*Celtis occidentalis,* 399a.	Common Hackberry
11, 45	*Cercidiphyllum japonicum,* 41a., 312a.	Katsuratree
31	*Cercis canadensis,* 202a.	Eastern Redbud

Pages	Scientific name	Common name
42, 60	*Chaenomeles japonica,* 283b., 423b.	Japanese Floweringquince
42, 60	*Chaenomeles speciosa,* 283a., 423a.	Common Floweringquince
74	*Chamaecyparis lawsoniana,* G60b.	Lawson Falsecypress, Port Oxford Cedar
74	*Chamaecyparis nootkatensis,* G61a.	Nootka Falsecypress, Alaska-Cedar
74	*Chamaecyparis obtusa,* G60a.	Hinoki Falsecypress
74	*Chamaecyparis pisifera,* G58a.	Sawara or Japanese Falsecypress
11, 41	*Chionanthus retusus,* 40b., 276b.	Chinese Fringetree
11, 37, 41	*Chionanthus virginicus,* 40a., 243a., 276a.	White Fringetree
27	*Cladrastis kentuckia* (lutea), 161b.	American Yellowwood
13	*Clematis × jackmanii,* 54b.	Jackman Clematis
64	*Clethra alnifolia,* 449a.	Summersweet Clethra
60	*Comptonia peregrina,* 420b.	Sweetfern
22	*Cornus alba,* 121a.	Tatarian Dogwood
37, 39	*Cornus alternifolia,* 242a., 262b.	Pagoda Dogwood
21	*Cornus amomum,* 117b.	Silky Dogwood
7	*Cornus canadensis,* 6b.	Bunchberry
11, 22	*Cornus florida,* 38a., 122a.	Flowering Dogwood
11, 21	*Cornus kousa,* 39a., 115a.	Kousa Dogwood
11, 21	*Cornus mas,* 39b., 118a.	Corneliancherry Dogwood
22	*Cornus racemosa,* 122b.	Gray Dogwood
21	*Cornus sanguinea,* 117a.	Bloodtwig Dogwood
22	*Cornus sericea (stolonifera),* 121b.	Redosier Dogwood
21	*Cornus sericea* 'Flaviramea', 119a.	Golden-Twig Dogwood
64	*Corylus americana,* 447a.	American Filbert, Hazelnut
64	*Corylus avellana,* 448b.	European Filbert
64	*Corylus avellana* 'Contorta', 448a.	Harry Lauder's Walkingstick
52, 54	*Corylus colurna,* 363a., 378a.	Turkish Filbert
41	*Cotinus coggygria,* 273a.	Common Smoketree, Smokebush
41	*Cotinus obovatus,* 273b.	American Smoketree
38	*Cotoneaster apiculatus,* 251a.	Cranberry Cotoneaster

Page	Scientific name	Common name
38	*Cotoneaster dammeri,* 253a.	Bearberry Cotoneaster
38	*Cotoneaster divaricatus,* 253b.	Spreading Cotoneaster
38	*Cotoneaster horizontalis,* 252a.	Rockspray or Rock Cotoneaster
39	*Cotoneaster lucidus,* 258b.	Hedge Cotoneaster
39	*Cotoneaster multiflorus,* 258a.	Many-flowered Cotoneaster
39	*Cotoneaster salicifolius,* 263a.	Willowleaf Cotoneaster
52	*Crataegus,* 366b. note	Hawthorn
43	*Crataegus crusgalli,* 289a.	Cockspur Hawthorn
52	*Crataegus crusgalli* var. *inermis,* 365a.	
43	*Crataegus* × *lavallei,* 290a.	Lavalle Hawthorn
43, 52, 58	*Crataegus mollis,* 288b., 366b., 409b.	Downy Hawthorn
43	*Crataegus phaenopyrum,* 288a.	Washington Hawthorn
43, 52, 58	*Crataegus viridis,* 290b., 366a., 408b.	Green Hawthorn
72	*Cryptomeria japonica,* G44a.	Japanese Cryptomeria, Japanese Cedar
25	*Cytisus scoparius,* 148a.	Scotch Broom, Common Broom
38	*Daphne cneorum,* 250a.	Rose Daphne
38	*Daphne* × *burkwoodii,* 250b.	Burkwood Daphne
41	*Daphne odora,* 274b.	Fragrant Daphne, Winter Daphne
46	*Davidia involucrata,* 315a.	Dove Tree, Handkerchief Tree
18	*Deutzia gracilis,* 94a.	Slender Deutzia
18	*Deutzia* × *lemoinei,* 94b.	Lemoine Deutzia
18	*Deutzia* × *magnifica,* 95a.	Showy Deutzia
18	*Deutzia scabra,* 95b.	Fuzzy Deutzia
15	*Diervilla sessilifolia,* 69a.	Southern Bush-honeysuckle
37	*Diospyros virginiana,* 245a.	Common Persimmon
31	*Elaeagnus,* 203a.	Oleaster
31	*Elaeagnus angustifolia,* 200a.	Russian-Olive
31	*Elaeagnus pungens,* 201b.	Thorny Elaeagnus
31	*Elaeagnus umbellata,* 201a.	Autumn-Olive, Autumn Elaeagnus
41	*Enkianthus campanulatus,* 278a.	Redvein Enkianthus

6	*Erica,* 3a.	Heath
55	*Eucommia ulmoides,* 391a.	Hardy Rubber Tree, Rubber Tree
15, 61	*Euonymus alatus,* 70a., 424a.	Winged Euonymus, Burning Bush
61	*Euonymus alatus* 'Compactus', 424a.	
11, 17	*Euonymus europaeus,* 42a., 87a.	European Euonymus
7, 17	*Euonymus fortunei,* 13b., 88b.	Wintercreeper Euonymus
41, 64	*Exochorda racemosa,* 275a., 451a.	Common Pearlbush
54	*Fagus grandifolia,* 380a.	American Beech
54	*Fagus sylvatica,* 380b.	European Beech
40, 63	*Forsythia europaea,* 270a., 443a.	Albanian Forsythia
17	*Forsythia* × *intermedia,* 90a.	Border Forsythia
17, 40, 63	*Forsythia ovata,* 90b., 270b., 443b.	Early Forsythia
17	*Forsythia suspensa* var. *sieboldii,* 89a.	Weeping Forsythia
17	*Forsythia viridissima,* 86a.	Greenstem Forysthia
17	*F. viridissima* 'Bronxensis', 88a.	
45	*Fothergilla gardenii,* 306a.	Dwarf Fothergilla
45	*Fothergilla major,* 306b.	Large Fothergilla
54, 63	*Franklinia alatamaha,* 376a., 439a.	Franklinia, Franklin Tree
13	*Fraxinus americana,* 53b.	White Ash
13	*Fraxinus excelsior,* 52a.	Common Ash, European Ash
12	*F. excelsior* 'Hessei', 43a.	
13	*Fraxinus pennsylvanica,* 53a.	Green Ash
13	*Fraxinus quadrangulata,* 51a.	Blue Ash
32, 41, 66	*Ginkgo biloba,* 205a., 277a., G1a.	Ginkgo, Maidenhair Tree
26, 28	*Gleditsia triacanthos* var. *inermis,* 159b., 172a.	Thornless Honeylocust
26	*Gymnocladus dioicus,* 159a.	Kentucky Coffeetree
57	*Halesia carolina,* 398b.	Carolina Silverbell
45	*Hamamelis* × *intermedia,* 308b.	
45	*Hamamelis japonica,* 310b.	Japanese Witchhazel
45	*Hamamelis mollis,* 308a.	Chinese Witchhazel
45	*Hamamelis vernalis,* 310a.	Vernal Witchhazel

45	*Hamamelis virginiana,* 309a.	Common Witchhazel
30	*Hedera helix,* 190b.	English Ivy
44	*Hibiscus syriacus,* 299a.	Shrub Althea, Rose of Sharon
14	*Hydrangea,* 63b.	
14	*Hydrangea arborescens,* 66a.	Smooth Hydrangea
14	*Hydrangea macrophylla,* 66b.	Bigleaf Hydrangea
14	*Hydrangea paniculata,* 65a.	Panicle Hydrangea
14	*Hydrangea quercifolia,* 64a.	Oakleaf Hydrangea
20	*Hypericum frondosum,* 106b.	Golden St. Johnswort
20	*Hypericum kalmianum,* 105a.	Kalm St. Johnswort
20	*Hypericum prolificum,* 106a.	Shrubby St. Johnswort
47	*Ilex* × *altaclarensis,* 325b.	Altaclara Holly
47	*Ilex aquifolium,* 325a.	English Holly
47	*Ilex cornuta,* 323a.	Chinese Holly
61	*Ilex crenata,* 428b.	Japanese Holly
54, 62	*Ilex decidua,* 376b., 435a.	Possumhaw
39, 61	*Ilex glabra,* 256a., 428a.	Inkberry
47	*Ilex* × *meserveae,* 326b.	Meserve Holly
47	*Ilex opaca,* 326a.	American Holly
36	*Ilex pedunculosa,* 240b.	Longstalk Holly
62, 63	*Ilex verticillata,* 435b., 442a.	Common Winterberry, Black Alder, Coralberry, Michigan Holly
56, 61	*Ilex vomitoria,* 392a., 432a.	Yaupon
28	*Juglans nigra,* 174b.	Black Walnut
27, 28	*Juglans regia,* 161a., 174a.	English Walnut, Persian Walnut
73	*Juniperus chinensis,* G55b.	Chinese Juniper
73	*Juniperus communis,* G50a.	Common Juniper
73	*Juniperus conferta,* G50b.	Shore Juniper
73	*Juniperus horizontalis,* G53b.	Creeping Juniper
73	*Juniperus horizontalis* 'Wiltonii', G53b.	Blue Rug Juniper
72	*Juniperus procumbens,* G49a.	Japgarden Juniper
73	*Juniperus sabina,* G54b.	Savin Juniper
72, 73	*J. sabina* var. *tamariscifolia,* G47a., G54a.	
73	*Juniperus scopulorum,* G52b.	Rocky Mountain Juniper, Colorado Redcedar
72	*Juniperus squamata,* G49b.	Singleseed Juniper
73	*Juniperus virginiana,* G55a.	Eastern Redcedar
39	*Kalmia latifolia,* 262a.	Mountain-laurel Kalmia, Mountain-laurel

42	*Kalopanax pictus,* 281a.	Castor-aralia
42	*K. pictus* var. *maximowiczii,* 281b.	
62	*Kerria japonica,* 437a.	Japanese Kerria
28	*Koelreuteria paniculata,* 170b.	Panicled Goldenraintree, Varnish Tree
18	*Kolkwitzia amabilis,* 96a.	Beautybush
25	*Laburnum × watereri,* 148b.	Goldenchain Tree, Waterer Laburnum
7, 10, 36, 38	*Lagerstroemia indica,* 6a., 36a., 236a., 255a.	Common Crapemyrtle
69	*Larix decidua,* G20b.	European Larch
69	*Larix kaempferi,* G20a.	Japanese Larch
63	*Leucothoe fontanesiana,* 444a.	Drooping Leucothoe, Fetterbush
24	*Ligustrum amurense,* 142b.	Amur Privet
24	*Ligustrum japonicum,* 136a.	Japanese Privet
24	*Ligustrum obtusifolium,* 142a.	Border Privet
20	*Ligustrum × vicaryi,* 107a.	Golden Vicary Privet, Golden privet
24	*Ligustrum vulgare,* 141a.	European Privet
34	*Lindera benzoin,* 221a.	Spicebush
51	*Liquidambar styraciflua,* 360a.	Sweetgum
32	*Liriodendron tulipifera,* 207a.	Tuliptree, Yellow Poplar
23	*Lonicera fragrantissima,* 129a.	Winter Honeysuckle
8	*Lonicera × heckrottii,* 15a.	Goldflame Honeysuckle
7	*Lonicera japonica,* 14b.	Japanese Honeysuckle
23	*Lonicera maackii,* 130a.	Amur Honeysuckle
23	*Lonicera morrowii,* 132b.	Morrow Honeysuckle
8	*Lonicera sempervirens,* 15b.	Trumpet Honeysuckle
23	*Lonicera tatarica,* 131a.	Tatarian Honeysuckle
23	*Lonicera × xylosteoides,* 133b.	
23	*Lonicera xylosteum,* 133a.	European Fly Honeysuckle
31, 37	*Maclura pomifera,* 197a., 246b.	Osage-orange,Hedge-apple
33	*Magnolia acuminata,* 216a.	Cucumbertree Magnolia
33	*Magnolia denudata (heptapeta),* 218a.	Yulan Magnolia
33	*Magnolia liliflora (quinquepeta),* 217a.	Lily Magnolia
33	*Magnolia × loebneri,* 214a.	Loebner Magnolia
32	*Magnolia macrophylla,* 209b.	Bigleaf Magnolia

33	*Magnolia × soulangiana,* 218b.	Saucer Magnolia
33	*Magnolia stellata,* 214b.	Star Magnolia
32	*Magnolia tripetala,* 209a.	Umbrella Magnolia
33	*Magnolia virginiana,* 213a.	Sweetbay Magnolia, Laurel Magnolia Swamp Magnolia
27	*Mahonia aquifolium,* 167a.	Oregongrapeholly, Oregon Hollygrape
60	*Malus spp.,* 417b.	Flowering Crabapple
30	*Menispermum canadense,* 192a.	Common Moonseed
72	*Metasequoia glypto-stroboides,* G43a.	Dawn Redwood
74	*Microbiota decussata,* G57b.	Russian Arborvitae
43, 51, 58	*Morus alba,* 295a., 361a., 405a., 408a.	Common Mulberry, White Mulberry
55	*Morus australis,* 390a.	
43, 51, 58	*Morus rubra,* 295b., 361b., 405b., 409a.	Red Mulberry
34, 63	*Myrica pensylvanica,* 222b., 440a.	Northern Bayberry
37	*Nyssa sylvatica,* 242b.	Black Gum, Black Tupelo, Sour Gum
57	*Ostrya virginiana,* 402a.	Hophornbeam, Ironwood
37, 58	*Oxydendrum arboreum,* 246a., 404a.	Sourwood, Sorrel Tree
30	*Pachysandra procumbens,* 187a.	Alleghany Pachysandra
30	*Pachysandra terminalis,* 187b.	Japanese Pachysandra
44	*Parrotia persica,* 304a.	Persian Parrotia
25	*Parthenocissus quinquefolia,* 150a.	Virginia Creeper, Woodbine
30	*Parthenocissus tricuspidata,* 190a.	Boston Ivy, Japanese Creeper
10	*Paulownia tomentosa,* 35a.	Royal Paulownia, Princess or Empress Tree
7	*Paxistima canbyi,* 10a.	Canby Paxistima, Rat-stripper
12	*Phellodendron amurense,* 49a.	Amur Corktree
16	*Philadelphus coronarius,* 81a.	Sweet Mockorange
16	*Philadelphus × virginalis,* 81b.	

44	*Physocarpus opulifolius,* 299b.	Common or Eastern Ninebark
69	*Picea abies,* G24a.	Norway Spruce
69	*Picea glauca,* G26b.	White Spruce
70	*Picea glauca* 'Conica', G27a.	Dwarf Alberta Spruce
70	*Picea glauca* 'Densata', G27b.	Black Hills Spruce
71	*Picea omorika,* G38a.	Serbian Spruce
69	*Picea orientalis,* G25a.	Oriental Spruce
70	*Picea pungens,* G28b.	Colorado Spruce
70	*Picea pungens* 'Glauca', G28a.	Blue Colorado Spruce
62	*Pieris japonica,* 436b.	Japanese Pieris, Andromeda
68	*Pinus aristata,* G13a.	Bristlecone Pine
66	*Pinus bungeana,* G4a.	Lacebark Pine
68	*Pinus cembra,* G16a.	Swiss Stone Pine
67	*Pinus densiflora,* G9a.	Japanese Red Pine
68	*Pinus flexilis,* G14a.	Limber Pine
67	*Pinus mugo,* G8b.	Swiss Mountain Pine, Mugo Pine
67	*Pinus nigra,* G11a.	Austrian Pine
68	*Pinus parviflora,* G16b.	Japanese White Pine
67	*Pinus resinosa,* G11b.	Red Pine
68	*Pinus strobus,* G15a.	Eastern White Pine, White Pine
67	*Pinus sylvestris,* G8a.	Scotch Pine
67	*Pinus thunbergiana,* G10a.	Japanese Black Pine
67	*Pinus virginiana,* G7a.	Virginia Pine, Scrub Pine
68	*Pinus wallichiana,* G12a.	Himalayan Pine, Bhutan Pine
51	*Platanus × acerifolia,* 358b.	London Planetree
51	*Platanus occidentalis,* 358a.	Sycamore, American Planetree
30	*Polygonum aubertii,* 193b.	Silvervine Fleeceflower, Silver Lace Vine
30	*Polygonum baldschuanicum,* 193b.	Bokaravine Fleeceflower
32	*Polygonum cuspidatum* var. *compactum,* 204a.	Low Japanese Fleeceflower
43	*Populus alba,* 292a.	White Poplar, Silver-leaved Poplar
55	*Populus deltoides,* 389b.	Eastern Cottonwood
55	*Populus nigra* 'Italica', 389a.	Lombardy Poplar
46	*Populus tremuloides,* 313a.	Quaking Aspen

26	*Potentilla fruticosa,* 155a.	Bush Cinquefoil
57, 64	*Prunus,* 401b., 453a.	Cherry, Peach, Plum, Apricot, Almond
50	*Prunus campanulata,* 348b.	Bell-flowered Cherry, Taiwan Cherry
32	*Prunus caroliniana,* 212b.	Carolina Cherrylaurel
48, 49	*Prunus cerasifera,* 335b., 343b.	Cherry Plum, Myrobalan Plum
61	*Prunus × cistena,* 425a.	Purpleleaf Sand Cherry
48	*Prunus glandulosa,* 332a.	Dwarf Flowering Almond
49	*Prunus* 'Hally Jolivette', 343a.	
32, 33, 49	*Prunus laurocerasus,* 212a., 215b., 338a.	Common Cherrylaurel, English Laurel
48	*Prunus maackii,* 333a.	Amur Chokecherry
50	*Prunus nigra,* 345a.	Canada Plum
48	*Prunus padus,* 337a.	European Birdcherry
50	*Prunus pensylvanica,* 348a.	Pin Cherry, Wild Red Cherry
49	*Prunus persica,* 339a.	Common Peach
49	*Prunus sargentii,* 340a.	Sargent Cherry
49	*Prunus serotina,* 341a.	Black Cherry
49	*Prunus serrulata,* 341b.	Japanese Flowering Cherry, Oriental Cherry
50	*Prunus subhirtella,* 346a.	Higan Cherry
50, 62	*Prunus tenella,* 347a., 436a.	Dwarf Russian Almond
50	*Prunus tomentosa,* 346b.	Manchu Cherry, Nanking Cherry
44	*Prunus triloba* var. *multiplex,* 297a.	Double Flowering Plum, Flowering Almond
48	*Prunus virginiana* 'Schubert', 335a.	
48	*Prunus × yedoensis,* 333b.	Yoshino Cherry
68	*Pseudolarix kaempferi,* G18b.	Golden-larch
70	*Pseudotsuga menziesii,* G29a.	Douglasfir
31, 42	*Pyracantha coccinea,* 199b., 285a.	Scarlet Firethorn
46, 56	*Pyrus calleryana* 'Bradford', 315b., 396a.	Bradford Callery Pear
51, 53	*Quercus,* 356a., 367a.	Oak
34	*Quercus acutissima,* 227a.	Sawtooth Oak
35	*Quercus alba,* 233a.	White Oak
35	*Quercus bicolor,* 234a.	Swamp White Oak
35	*Quercus coccinea,* 230a.	Scarlet Oak
34	*Quercus imbricaria,* 225a.	Shingle Oak, Laurel Oak

35	*Quercus lyrata,* 235b.	Overcup Oak
35	*Quercus macrocarpa,* 235a.	Bur Oak, Mossycup Oak
34	*Quercus muehlenbergii,* 227b.	Chinkapin Oak, Yellow Chestnut Oak
35	*Quercus palustris,* 231a.	Pin Oak
35	*Quercus robur,* 232a.	English Oak
35	*Quercus rubra,* 231b.	Red Oak
35	*Quercus velutina,* 229a.	Black Oak
37	*Rhamnus caroliniana,* 244a.	Carolina Buckthorn, Indian Cherry
42	*Rhamnus cathartica,* 284a.	Common Buckthorn
36, 39	*Rhamnus frangula,* 240a., 261b.	Glossy Buckthorn
60	*Rhamnus frangula* 'Asplenifolia', 420a.	
36, 39	*Rhamnus frangula* 'Columnaris', 238a., 261a.	Tallhedge Buckthorn
40	*Rhododendron carolinianum,* 266b.	Carolina Rhododendron
40	*Rhododendron catawbiense,* 267a.	Catawba Rhododendron
40	*Rhododendron mucronulatum,* 268a.	Korean Rhododendron
40	*Rhododendron schlippen-bachii,* 268b.	Royal Azalea
40	*Rhododendron* 'P.J.M.', 266a.	P.J.M. Rhododendron
15	*Rhodotypos scandens,* 67a.	Black Jetbead
25	*Rhus aromatica,* 147b.	Fragrant Sumac
26	*Rhus copallina,* 156a.	Flameleaf Sumac, Shining Sumac
26, 29	*Rhus glabra,* 157b., 178a.	Smooth Sumac
26, 29	*Rhus typhina,* 157a., 178b.	Staghorn Sumac
28	*Rhus typhina* 'Dissecta', 170a.	
44	*Ribes alpinum,* 300a.	Alpine Currant
44	*Ribes odoratum,* 300b.	Clove Currant
27	*Robinia fertilis,* 164a.	
27	*Robinia hispida,* 164b.	Bristly Locust, Roseacacia Locust
27	*Robinia pseudoacacia,* 163b.	Black Locust
25, 27	*Rosa,* 147a., 166a.	Rose
53	*Salix alba,* 374b.	White Willow
53	*Salix alba* 'Tristis', 374a.	Golden Weeping Willow
53	*Salix caprea,* 369b.	Goat Willow

53	*Salix discolor,* 369b.	Pussy Willow
53	*Salix matsudana,* 373b.	Hankow Willow
53	*Salix matsudana* 'Tortuosa', 373a.	Corkscrew Hankow Willow
53	*Salix purpurea,* 372a.	Purpleosier Willow
53	*Salix purpurea* 'Nana', 372b.	Artic Blue Leaf Willow
12	*Sambucus canadensis,* 48b.	American Elder, Elderberry
34	*Sassafras albidum,* 222a.	Common Sassafras
68	*Sciadopitys verticillata,* G17a.	Umbrella-pine, Japanese Umbrella Pine
27	*Sophora japonica,* 162a.	Japanese Pagoda Tree, Scholar-tree
54, 60	*Sorbus alnifolia,* 382a., 417a.	Korean Mountainash
29	*Sorbus aria,* 180b.	Whitebeam Mountainash
29	*Sorbus aucuparia,* 180a.	European Mountainash, Rowan
65	*Spiraea* × *bumalda,* 455a.	Bumald Spiraea
64, 65	*Spiraea japonica,* 449b., 455b.	Japanese Spiraea
62	*Spiraea nipponica* 'Snowmound', 433b.	Snowmound Nippon Spiraea
62	*Spiraea prunifolia,* 433a.	Bridalwreath Spiraea
61	*Spiraea thunbergii,* 430a.	Thunberg Spiraea
44, 60, 65	*Spiraea* × *vanhouttei,* 297b., 421a., 454a.	Vanhoutte Spiraea
12	*Staphylea trifolia,* 46b.	American Bladdernut
60	*Stephanandra incisa,* 421b.	Cutleaf Stephanandra
56, 64	*Stewartia ovata,* 394a., 452a.	Mountain Stewartia
24	*Symphoricarpos albus,* 140a., 140b.	Common Snowberry
24	*Symphoricarpos* × *chenaultii,* 139a.	Chenault Coralberry
24	*Symphoricarpos orbiculatus,* 139b.	Indiancurrant Coralberry, Buckbrush
22	*Syringa* × *chinensis,* 126b.	Chinese lilac
22	*Syringa meyeri,* 127a.	Meyer Lilac
22	*Syringa patula,* 127b.	Manchurian Lilac
22	*Syringa reticulata,* 124a.	Japanese Tree Lilac
24	*Syringa sweginzowii,* 136b.	Chengtu Lilac
23	*Syringa villosa,* 135a.	Late Lilac
22	*Syringa vulgaris,* 126a.	Common Lilac
29	*Tamarix,* 181a.	Tamarisk, Tamarix
72	*Taxodium distichum,* G43b.	Common Baldcypress

71	*Taxus baccata,* G41a.	English Yew, Common Yew
71	*Taxus cuspidata,* G42a.	Japanese Yew
71	*Taxus × media,* G42b.	Anglojap Yew
75	*Thuja occidentalis,* G62b.	Eastern Arborvitae, White Cedar
74	*Thuja occidentalis* 'Pendula', G61b.	
75	*Thuja (Platycladus) orientalis,* G62a.	Oriental Arborvitae
74	*Thuja plicata,* G58b.	Giant Arborvitae, Western Arborvitae
46	*Tilia americana,* 317a.	American Linden, Basswood
46	*Tilia cordata,* 318b.	Littleleaf Linden
46	*Tilia × euchlora,* 318a.	Crimean Linden
46	*Tilia heterophylla,* 319a.	Beetree Linden, White Basswood
43	*Tilia mongolica,* 294b.	Mongolian Linden
46	*Tilia petiolaris,* 321b.	Pendant Silver Linden
46	*Tilia platyphyllos,* 320a.	Bigleaf Linden
46	*Tilia tomentosa,* 321a.	Silver Linden
71	*Tsuga canadensis,* G39b.	Canadian Hemlock, Eastern Hemlock
71	*Tsuga caroliniana,* G39a.	Carolina Hemlock
59	*Ulmus americana,* 415a.	American Elm, White Elm
59	*Ulmus carpinifolia,* 416b.	Smoothleaf Elm
59	*Ulmus glabra,* 416a.	Scotch Elm
59	*Ulmus parvifolia,* 414a.	Chinese Elm, Lacebark Elm
59	*Ulmus pumila,* 414b.	Siberian Elm
39	*Vaccinium arboreum,* 257b.	Farkleberry
40, 64	*Vaccinium corymbosum,* 271a., 450a.	Highbush Blueberry
38, 61	*Vaccinium macrocarpon,* 254a., 429a.	American Cranberry
29	*Vaccinium vitis-idaea,* 186a.	Cowberry
29	*Vaccinium vitis-idaea* var. minus, 186b.	Mountain Cranberry
16	*Viburnum × burkwoodii,* 79a.	Burkwood Viburnum
16	*Viburnum carlesii,* 78a.	Koreanspice Viburnum
16	*Viburnum × carlcephalum,* 79b.	Fragrant Viburnum, Carlcephalum Viburnum
19	*Viburnum cassinoides,* 102a.	Witherod Viburnum
18	*Viburnum dentatum,* 91a.	Arrowwood Viburnum
18	*Viburnum dilatatum,* 96b.	Linden Viburnum

19	*Viburnum farreri,* 103a.	Fragrant Viburnum
16	*Viburnum × juddii,* 78b.	Judd Virburnum
16	*Viburnum lantana,* 76a.	Wayfaringtree Viburnum
19	*Viburnum lentago,* 101a.	Nannyberry Viburnum, Sheepberry
16, 20	*Viburnum macrocephalum,* 76b., 112b.	Chinese Snowball Viburnum
19	*Viburnum opulus,* 99a.	European Cranberrybush Viburnum
15	*Viburnum plicatum* var. *tomentosum,* 72a.	Doublefile Viburnum
19	*Viburnum prunifolium,* 103b.	Blackhaw Viburnum
15, 21	*Viburnum × rhytido-phylloides,* 74b., 113b.	Lantanophyllum Viburnum
15, 21	*Viburnum rhytidophyllum,* 74a., 113a.	Leatherleaf Viburnum
19	*Viburnum sargentii,* 98a.	Sargent Viburnum
18	*Viburnum setigerum,* 91b.	Tea Viburnum
19	*Viburnum sieboldii,* 100a.	Siebold Viburnum
19	*Viburnum trilobum,* 99b.	American Cranberrybush Viburnum
7	*Vinca major,* 12b.	Large Periwinkle
7	*Vinca minor,* 12a.	Common Periwinkle
15	*Weigela florida,* 69b.	Old Fashioned Weigela
25	*Wisteria floribunda,* 151a.	Japanese Wisteria
28	*Xanthorhiza simplicissima,* 169a.	Yellowroot
59	*Zelkova serrata,* 413a.	Japanese Zelkova

COMMON NAME INDEX

The number preceding the common name is the page number on which it can be found.

The number(s) following the common name refer to the couplet number.

G preceding a couplet number indicates gymnosperm key

Number without prefix indicates angiosperm key

30 Actinidia, Bower, 194a. — *Actinidia arguta*
25 Akebia, Fiveleaf Akebia, 150b. — *Akebia quinata*
Alder
- 44, 62, 63 Black Alder, 303a., 435b., 442a. — *Alnus glutinosa* or *Ilex verticillata*
- 44 Common, 303a. — *Alnus glutinosa*
- 44 European, 303a. — *Alnus glutinosa*
- 44 Grey, 303b. — *Alnus incana*
- 44 White, 303b. — *Alnus incana*

20 Allspice, Carolina, 110a. — *Calycanthus floridus*
Almond
- 48 Dwarf Flowering Almond, 332a. — *Prunus glandulosa*
- 50, 62 Dwarf Russian Almond, 347a., 436a. — *Prunus tenella*
- 44 Flowering Almond, 297a. — *Prunus triloba* var. *multiplex*

44 Althea, Shrub, 299a. — *Hibiscus syriacus*
30 Ampelopsis, Porcelain, 189a. — *Ampelopsis brevipedunculata*
62 Andromeda, 436b. — *Pieris japonica*
57, 64 Apricot, 401b., 453a. — *Prunus*
25 Aralia, Fiveleaf, 149a. — *Acanthopanax sieboldianus*
Arborvitae
- 75 American, G62b. — *Thuja occidentalis*
- 75 Eastern, G62b. — *Thuja occidentalis*
- 74 Giant, G58b. — *Thuja plicata*
- 75 Oriental, G62a. — *Thuja (Platycladus) orientalis*

Page	Common Name	Scientific Name
74	Russian, G57b.	*Microbiota decussata*
74	Western, G58b.	*Thuja plicata*
	Ash	
13	Blue, 51a.	*Fraxinus quadrangulata*
13	Common, 52a.	*Fraxinus excelsior*
13	European, 52a.	*Fraxinus excelsior*
13	Green, 53a.	*Fraxinus pennsylvanica*
13	Red, 53a.	*Fraxinus pennsylvanica*
13	White, 53b.	*Fraxinus americana*
46	Aspen, Quaking, 313a.	*Populus tremuloides*
40	Azalea, Royal, 268b.	*Rhododendron schlippenbachii*
72	Baldcypress, G43b.	*Taxodium distichum*
	Barberry	
31	Japanese, 198a.	*Berberis thunbergii*
42	Mentor, 286b.	*Berberis* × *mentorensis*
	Basswood	
46	American, 317a.	*Tilia americana*
46	White, 319a.	*Tilia heterophylla*
34, 63	Bayberry, Northern, 222b., 440a.	*Myrica pensylvanica*
29	Bearberry, 185b.	*Arctostaphylos uva-ursi*
29	Bear's Grape, 185b.	*Arctostaphylos uva-ursi*
18	Beautybush, 96a.	*Kolkwitzia amabilis*
	Beech	
54	American, 380a.	*Fagus grandifolia*
54	Blue, 383b.	*Carpinus caroliniana*
54	European, 380b.	*Fagus sylvatica*
	Birch	
50	Asian White, 352b.	*Betula platyphylla* var. *japonica*
57	Black, 401a.	*Betula lenta*
51	Canoe, 353a.	*Betula papyrifera*
57	Cherry, 401a.	*Betula lenta*
50, 51	European White, 352a., 353b.	*Betula pendula*
50	Gray, 351a.	*Betula populifolia*
51	Paper, 353a.	*Betula papyrifera*
52, 56	River, 364b., 395a.	*Betula nigra*
50, 51	White, 351a., 353a.	*Betula papyrifera* or *Betula populifolia*
48	Birdcherry, European, 337a.	*Prunus padus*
30	Bittersweet, American, 194b.	*Celastrus scandens*
12	Bladdernut, American, 46b.	*Staphylea trifolia*

40, 64	Blueberry, Highbush, 271a., 450a.	*Vaccinium corymbosum*
12	Boxelder, 50a.	*Acer negundo*
25	Broom, Scotch, 148a.	*Cytisus scoparius*
	Boxwood	
20	Common, 109b.	*Buxus sempervirens*
20	Littleleaf, 109a.	*Buxus microphylla*
24	Buckbrush, 139b.	*Symphoricarpos orbiculatus*
	Buckeye	
14	Bottlebrush, 58a.	*Aesculus parviflora*
14	Ohio, 60a.	*Aesculus glabra*
14	Red, 59a.	*Aesculus pavia*
14	Yellow, 60b.	*Aesculus flava (octandra)*
	Buckthorn	
37	Carolina, 244a.	*Rhamnus caroliniana*
42	Common, 284a.	*Rhamnus cathartica*
36, 39	Glossy, 240a., 261b.	*Rhamnus frangula*
36, 39	Tallhedge, 238a., 261a.	*Rhamnus frangula* 'Columnaris'
7	Bunchberry, 6b.	*Cornus canadensis*
15	Bush-honeysuckle, Southern, 69a.	*Diervilla sessilifolia*
14	Butterfly-bush, 63a.	*Buddleia davidii*
42	Castor-aralia, 281a.	*Kalopanax pictus*
	Catalpa	
6	Northern, 5a.	*Catalpa speciosa*
6	Southern, 5b.	*Catalpa bignonioides*
	Cedar	
69	Atlas, G21a.	*Cedrus atlantica*
74	Alaska, G61a.	*Chamaecyparis nootkatensis*
68	Cedar of Lebanon, G19a.	*Cedrus libani*
72	Japanese, G44a.	*Cryptomeria japonica*
74	Port Orford, G60b.	*Chamaecyparis lawsoniana*
75	White, G62b.	*Thuja occidentalis*
	Cherry	
50	Bell-flowered, 348b.	*Prunus campanulata*
49	Black, 341a.	*Prunus serotina*
50	Higan, 346a.	*Prunus subhirtella*
37	Indian, 244a.	*Rhamnus caroliniana*
49	Japanese Flowering, 341b.	*Prunus serrulata*
50	Manchu, 346b.	*Prunus tomentosa*
50	Nanking, 346b.	*Prunus tomentosa*

49	Oriental, 341b.	*Prunus serrulata*
50	Pin, 348a.	*Prunus pensylvanica*
61	Purpleleaf Sand, 425a.	*Prunus × cistena*
49	Sargent, 340a.	*Prunus sargentii*
50	Taiwan, 348b.	*Prunus campanulata*
48	Yoshino, 333b.	*Prunus × yedoensis*
	Cherrylaurel	
32	Carolina, 212b.	*Prunus caroliniana*
32, 33, 49	Common, 212a., 215b., 338a.	*Prunus laurocerasus*
56	Chestnut, Chinese, 394b.	*Castanea mollissima*
41	Chittamwood, 273b.	*Cotinus obovatus*
48	Chokecherry, Amur, 333a.	*Prunus maackii*
	Chokeberry	
48	Black, 331a.	*Aronia melancarpa*
48	Red, 331b.	*Aronia arbutifolia*
26	Cinquefoil, Bush, 155a.	*Potentilla fruticosa*
13	Clematis, Jackman, 54b.	*Clematis × jackmanii*
64	Clethra, Summersweet, 449a.	*Clethra alnifolia*
26	Coffeetree, Kentucky, 159a.	*Gymnocladus dioicus*
	Coralberry	
24	Chenault, 139a.	*Symphoricarpos × chenaultii*
24	Indiancurrant, 139b.	*Symphoricarpos orbiculatus*
12	Corktree, Amur, 49a.	*Phellodendron amurense*
	Cotoneaster	
38	Bearberry, 253a.	*Cotoneaster dammeri*
38	Cranberry, 251a.	*Cotoneaster apiculatus*
39	Hedge, 258b.	*Cotoneaster lucidus*
39	Many-flowered, 258a.	*Cotoneaster multiflorus*
38	Rock, 252a.	*Cotoneaster horizontalis*
38	Rockspray, 252a.	*Cotoneaster horizontalis*
38	Spreading, 253b.	*Cotoneaster divaricatus*
39	Willowleaf, 263a.	*Cotoneaster salicifolius*
55	Cottonwood, Eastern, 389b.	*Populus deltoides*
29	Cowberry, 186a.	*Vaccinium vitis-idaea*
60	Crabapple, Flowering, 417b.	*Malus*
	Cranberry	
38, 61	American, 254a., 429a.	*Vaccinium macrocarpon*
29	Hog, 185b.	*Arctostaphylos uva-ursi*
29	Mountain, 186a.	*Vaccinium vitis-idaea*
7, 10, 36, 38	Crapemyrtle, Common, 6a., 36a., 236a., 255a.	*Lagerstroemia indica*

	Creeper	
30	Japanese, 190a.	*Parthenocissus tricuspidata*
25	Virginia, 150a.	*Parthenocissus quinquefolia*
72	Cryptomeria, Japanese, G44a.	*Cryptomeria japonica*
	Currant	
44	Alpine, 300a.	*Ribes alpinum*
44	Clove, 300b.	*Ribes odoratum*
74	Cypress, Yellow, G61a.	*Chamaecyparis nootkatensis*
	Daphne	
38	Burkwood, 250b.	*Daphne × burkwoodii*
41	Fragrant, 274b.	*Daphne odora*
38	Rose, 250a.	*Daphne cneorum*
41	Winter, 274b.	*Daphne odora*
	Deutzia	
18	Fuzzy, 95b.	*Deutzia scabra*
18	Lemoine, 94b.	*Deutzia × lemoinei*
18	Showy, 95a.	*Deutzia × magnifica*
18	Slender, 94a.	*Deutzia gracilis*
27	Devils-walkingstick, 166b.	*Aralia spinosa*
	Dogwood	
21	Bloodtwig, 117a.	*Cornus sanguinea*
11, 21	Corneliancherry, 39b., 118a.	*Cornus mas*
11, 22	Flowering, 38a., 122a.	*Cornus florida*
21	Golden-twig, 119a.	*Cornus sericea* 'Flaviramea'
22	Gray, 122b.	*Cornus racemosa*
11, 21	Kousa, 39a., 115a.	*Cornus kousa*
37, 39	Pagoda, 242a., 262b.	*Cornus alternifolia*
22	Redosier, 121b.	*Cornus sericea (C. stolonifera)*
21	Silky, 117b.	*Cornus amomum*
22	Tatarian, 121a.	*Cornus alba*
70	Douglasfir, G29a.	*Pseudotsuga menziesii*
46	Dove-tree, 315a.	*Davidia involucrata*
	Elaeagnus	
31	Autumn, 201a.	*Elaeagnus umbellata*
31	Thorny, 201b.	*Elaeagnus pungens*
12	Elder, American, 48b.	*Sambucus canadensis*
12	Elderberry, 48b.	*Sambucus canadensis*
	Elm	
59	American, 415a.	*Ulmus americana*
59	Chinese, 414a.	*Ulmus parvifolia*

59	Lacebark, 414a.	*Ulmus parvifolia*
59	Scotch, 416a.	*Ulmus glabra*
59	Siberian, 414b.	*Ulmus pumila*
59	Smoothleaf, 416b.	*Ulmus carpinifolia*
10	Empress Tree, 35a.	*Paulownia tomentosa*
41	Enkianthus, Redvein, 278a.	*Enkianthus campanulatus*
	Euonymus	
11, 17	European, 42a., 87a.	*Euonymus europaeus*
15, 61	Winged, 70a., 424a.	*Euonymus alatus*
7, 17	Wintercreeper, 13b., 88b.	*Euonymus fortunei*
	Falsecypress	
74	Hinoki, G60a.	*Chamaecyparis obtusa*
74	Japanese, G58a.	*Chamaecyparis pisifera*
74	Lawson, G60b.	*Chamaecyparis lawsoniana*
74	Nootka, G61a.	*Chamaecyparis nootkatensis*
74	Sawara, G58a.	*Chamaecyparis pisifera*
39	Farkleberry, 257b.	*Vaccinium arboreum*
63	Fetterbush, 444a.	*Leucothoe fontanesiana*
	Filbert	
64	American, 447a.	*Corylus americana*
64	European, 448b.	*Corylus avellana*
52, 54	Turkish, 363a., 378a.	*Corylus colurna*
	Fir	
71	Balsam, G36b.	*Abies balsamea*
70	Cilician, G32a.	*Abies cilicica*
70	Concolor, G33a.	*Abies concolor*
71	Fraser, G35a.	*Abies fraseri*
70	Nordmann, G32b.	*Abies nordmanniana*
71	Veitch, G35b., G36a.	*Abies veitchii*
70	White, G33a.	*Abies concolor*
31, 42	Firethorn, Scarlet, 199b., 285a.	*Pyracantha coccinea*
	Fleeceflower	
30	Bakaravine, 193b.	*Polygonum baldschuanicum*
32	Low Japanese, 204a.	*Polygonum cuspidatum* var. *compactum*
30	Silvervine, 193b.	*Polygonum aubertii*
	Floweringquince	
42, 60	Common, 283a., 423a.	*Chaenomeles speciosa*
42, 60	Japanese, 283b., 423b.	*Chaenomeles japonica*
	Forsythia	
40, 63	Albanian, 270a., 443a.	*Forsythia europaea*

17	Border, 90a.	*Forsythia* × *intermedia*
17, 40, 63	Early, 90b., 270b., 443b.	*Forsythia ovata*
17	Greenstem, 90a.	*Forsythia* × *intermedia*
17	Weeping, 89a.	*Forsythia suspensa* var. *sieboldii*
	Fringetree	
11, 41	Chinese, 40b., 276b.	*Chionanthus retusus*
11, 37, 41	White, 40a., 243a., 276a.	*Chionanthus virginicus*
	Fothergilla	
45	Dwarf, 306a.	*Fothergilla gardenii*
45	Major, 306b.	*Fothergilla major*
54, 63	Franklin Tree, 376a., 439a.	*Franklinia alatamaha*
32, 41, 66	Ginkgo, 205a., 277a., G1a.	*Ginkgo biloba*
25	Goldenchain Tree, 148b.	*Laburnum* × *watereri*
68	Golden-larch, G18b.	*Pseudolarix kaempferi*
28	Goldenraintree, Panicled, 170b.	*Koelreuteria paniculata*
27	Grapeholly, Oregon, 167a.	*Mahonia aquifolium*
	Gum	
37	Black, 242b.	*Nyssa sylvatica*
37	Sour, 242b.	*Nyssa sylvatica*
	Hackberry	
57	Common, 399a.	*Celtis occidentalis*
36, 57, 58	Southern, 239a., 399b., 410a.	*Celtis laevigata*
36, 57, 58	Sugar, 239a., 399b., 410a.	*Celtis laevigata*
46	Handkerchief Tree, 315a.	*Davidia involucrata*
55	Hardy Rubber Tree, 391a.	*Eucommia ulmoides*
	Hawthorn	
43	Cockspur, 289a.	*Crataegus crusgalli*
43, 52, 58	Downy, 288b., 366b., 409b.	*Crataegus mollis*
43, 52, 58	Green, 290b., 366a., 408b.	*Crataegus viridis*
43	Lavalle, 290a.	*Crataegus* × *lavallei*
43	Washington, 288a.	*Crataegus phaenopyrum*
64	Hazelnut, 447a.	*Corylus americana*
6	Heath, 3a.	*Erica*
7	Heather, Scotch, 8a.	*Calluna vulgaris*
	Hedge-apple	*Maclura pomifera*
	Hemlock	
71	Canadian, G39b.	*Tsuga canadensis*

71	Carolina, G39a.	*Tsuga caroliniana*
71	Eastern, G39b.	*Tsuga canadensis*
27	Hercules-club, 166b.	*Aralia spinosa*
	Hickory	
28	Shagbark, 176b.	*Carya ovata*
28	Shellbark, 176a.	*Carya laciniosa*
	Holly	
47	Altaclara, 325b.	*Ilex altaclarensis*
47	American, 326a.	*Ilex opaca*
47	Chinese, 323a.	*Ilex cornuta*
47	English, 325a.	*Ilex aquifolium*
61	Japanese, 428b.	*Ilex crenata*
36	Longstalk, 240b.	*Ilex pedunculosa*
47	Meserve, 326b.	*Ilex × meserveae*
62, 63	Michigan, 435b., 442a.	*Ilex verticillata*
27	Hollygrape, Oregon, 167a.	*Mahonia aquifolium*
26, 28	Honeylocust, Thornless, 159b., 172a.	*Gleditsia triacanthos* var. *inermis*
	Honeysuckle	
23	Amur, 130a.	*Lonicera maackii*
23	European Fly, 133a.	*Lonicera xylosteum*
8	Goldflame, 15a.	*Lonicera × heckrottii*
7	Japanese, 14b.	*Lonicera japonica*
23	Morrow, 132b.	*Lonicera morrowii*
23	Tatarian, 131a.	*Lonicera tatarica*
8	Trumpet, 15b.	*Lonicera sempervirens*
23	Winter, 129a.	*Lonicera fragrantissima*
	Hophornbeam, American	*Ostrya virginiana*
	Hornbeam	
54	American, 383a.	*Carpinus betulus*
54	European, 383a.	*Carpinus betulus*
	Horsechestnut	
13	Common, 57a.	*Aesculus hippocastanum*
13	European, 57a.	*Aesculus hippocastanum*
13	Red, 57b.	*Aesculus × carnea*
	Hydrangea	
14	Bigleaf, 66b.	*Hydrangea macrophylla*
14	Oakleaf, 64a.	*Hydrangea quercifolia*
14	Panicle, 65a.	*Hydrangea paniculata*
14	Smooth, 66a.	*Hydrangea arborescens*
39, 61	Inkberry, 256a., 428a.	*Ilex glabra*
54, 57	Ironwood, 383b., 402a.	*Carpinus caroliniana* or *Ostrya virginiana*

	Ivy	
30	Boston, 190a.	*Parthenocissus tricuspidata*
30	English, 190b.	*Hedera helix*
15	Jetbead, Black, 67a.	*Rhodotypos scandens*
55	Juneberry, 387b.	*Amelanchier arborea*
	Juniper	
73	Blue Rug, G53b.	*Juniperus horizontalis* 'Wiltonii'
73	Chinese, G53b.	*Juniperus horizontalis*
73	Common, G50a.	*Juniperus communis*
73	Creeping, G53b.	*Juniperus horizontalis*
72	Japgarden, G49a.	*Juniperus procumbens*
73	Rocky Mountain, G52b.	*Juniperus scopulorum*
73	Savin, G54b.	*Juniperus sabina*
73	Shore, G50b.	*Juniperus conferta*
72	Singleseed, G49b.	*Juniperus squamata*
39	Kalmia, Mountain-laurel, 262a.	*Kalmia latifolia*
11, 45	Katsuratree, 41a., 312a.	*Cercidiphyllum japonicum*
62	Kerria, Japanese, 437a.	*Kerria japonica*
29	Kinnikinick, 185b.	*Arctostaphylos uva-ursi*
25	Laburnum, Waterer, 148b.	*Laburnum × watereri*
	Larch	
69	Common, G20b.	*Larix decidua*
69	European, G20b.	*Larix decidua*
69	Japanese, G20a.	*Larix kaempferi*
32, 33, 49	Laurel, English, 212a., 215b., 338a.	*Prunus laurocerasus*
63	Leucothoe, Drooping, 444a.	*Leucothoe fontanesiana*
	Lilac	
24	Chengtu, 136b.	*Syringa sweginzowii*
22	Chinese, 126b.	*Syringa × chinensis*
22	Common, 126a.	*Syringa vulgaris*
22	Japanese Tree, 124a.	*Syringa reticulata*
23	Late, 135a.	*Syringa villosa*
22	Manchurian, 127b.	*Syringa patula*
22	Meyer, 127a.	*Syringa meyeri*
14	Summer, 63a.	*Buddleia davidii*
37, 58	Lily-of-the-Valley Tree, 246a., 404a.	*Oxydendrum arboreum*
	Linden	
46	American, 317a.	*Tilia americana*
46	Beetree, 319a.	*Tilia heterophylla*
46	Bigleaf, 320a.	*Tilia platyphyllos*

Page	Common name	Scientific name
46	Crimean, 318a.	*Tilia × euchlora*
46	Littleleaf, 318b.	*Tilia cordata*
43	Mongolian, 294b.	*Tilia mongolica*
46	Pendent Silver, 321b.	*Tilia petiolaris*
46	Silver, 321a.	*Tilia tomentosa*
	Locust	
27	Black, 163b.	*Robinia pseudoacacia*
27	Bristly, 164b.	*Robinia hispida*
27	Roseacacia, 164b.	*Robinia hispida*
	Magnolia	
32	Bigleaf, 209b.	*Magnolia macrophylla*
33	Cucumbertree, 216a.	*Magnolia acuminata*
33	Laurel, 213a.	*Magnolia virginiana*
33	Lily, 217a.	*Magnolia liliflora (quinquepeta)*
33	Loebner, 214a.	*Magnolia × loebneri*
33	Saucer, 218b.	*Magnolia × soulangiana*
33	Star, 214b.	*Magnolia stellata*
33	Swamp, 213a.	*Magnolia virginiana*
33	Sweetbay, 213a.	*Magnolia virginiana*
32	Umbrella, 209a.	*Magnolia tripetala*
33	Yulan, 218a.	*Magnolia denudata (heptapeta)*
32, 41, 66	Maidenhair Tree, 205a., 277a., G1a.	*Ginkgo biloba*
	Maple	
8	Amur, 22a.	*Acer ginnala*
9	Black, 30a.	*Acer nigrum*
12	Boxelder, 50a.	*Acer negundo*
9	Freeman, 32b.	*Acer × freemanii*
9	Fullmoon, 28b.	*Acer japonicum*
9	Hedge, 26b.	*Acer campestre*
9, 13	Japanese, 28a., 55a.	*Acer palmatum*
9	Miyabe, 26a.	*Acer miyabei*
9	Norway, 25b.	*Acer platanoides*
12	Paperbark, 46a.	*Acer griseum*
10	Planetree, 31a.	*Acer pseudoplatanus*
9	Purpleblow, 25a.	*Acer truncatum*
8, 10	Red, 20b., 32b.	*Acer rubrum*
9	Shantung, 25a.	*Acer truncatum*
10	Silver, 32a.	*Acer saccharinum*
8	Striped, 20a.	*Acer pensylvanicum*
9	Sugar, 30b.	*Acer saccharum*
10	Sycamore, 31a.	*Acer pseudoplatanus*

8, 12	Tatarian, 22b., 43b.	*Acer tataricum*
8	Trident, 19a.	*Acer buergeranum*
29	Mealberry, 185b.	*Arctostaphylos uva-ursi*
16	Mockorange, Sweet, 81a.	*Philadelphus coronarius*
30	Moonseed, Common, 192a.	*Menispermum canadense*
8	Moosewood, 20a.	*Acer pensylvanicum*
	Mountainash	
29	European, 180a.	*Sorbus aucuparia*
54, 60	Korean, 382a., 417a.	*Sorbus alnifolia*
29	Whitebeam, 180b.	*Sorbus aria*
39	Mountain-laurel, 262a.	*Kalmia latifolia*
	Mulberry	
43, 51, 58	Red, 295b., 361b., 405b., 409a.	*Morus rubra*
43, 51, 58	White, 295a., 361a., 405a., 408a.	*Morus alba*
54	Musclewood, 383b.	*Carpinus caroliniana*
44	Ninebark, 299b.	*Physocarpus opulifolius*
	Oak	
35	Black, 229a.	*Quercus velutina*
35	Bur, 235a.	*Quercus macrocarpa*
34	Chinkapin, 227b.	*Quercus muehlenbergii*
35	English, 232a.	*Quercus robur*
35	Overcup, 235b.	*Quercus lyrata*
35	Pin, 231a.	*Quercus palustris*
35	Red, 231b.	*Quercus rubra*
34	Sawtooth, 227a.	*Quercus acutissima*
35	Scarlet, 230a.	*Quercus coccinea*
34	Shingle, 225a.	*Quercus imbricaria*
35	Swamp White, 234a.	*Quercus bicolor*
35	White, 233a.	*Quercus alba*
	Olive	
31	Autumn, 201a.	*Elaeagnus umbellata*
31	Russian, 200a.	*Elaeagnus angustifolia*
27	Oregongrapeholly, 167a.	*Mahonia aquifolium*
31, 37	Osage-orange, 197a., 246b.	*Maclura pomifera*
	Pachysandra	
30	Alleghany, 187a.	*Pachysandra procumbens*
30	Japanese, 187b.	*Pachysandra terminalis*
27	Pagodatree, Japanese, 162a.	*Sophora japonica*
44	Parrotia, Persian, 304a.	*Parrotia persica*
34	Pawpaw, 219a.	*Asimina triloba*
10	Paulownia, Royal, 35a.	*Paulownia tomentosa*
7	Paxistima, Canby, 10a.	*Paxistima canbyi*

49	Peach, Common, 339a.	*Prunus persica*
46, 56	Pear, Bradford, 315b., 396a.	*Pyrus calleryana* 'Bradford'
41, 64	Pearlbush, 275a., 451a.	*Exochorda racemosa*
25	Peashrub, Siberian, 152a.	*Caragana arborescens*
29	Pecan, 179a.	*Carya illinoensis*
	Periwinkle	
7	Common, 12a.	*Vinca minor*
7	Large, 12b.	*Vinca major*
37	Persimmon, 245a.	*Diospyros virginiana*
62	Pieris, Japanese, 436b.	*Pieris japonica*
	Pine	
67	Austrian, G11a.	*Pinus nigra*
68	Bristlecone, G13a.	*Pinus aristata*
68	Eastern White, G15a.	*Pinus strobus*
68	Himalayan, G12a.	*Pinus wallichiana*
67	Japanese Black, G10a.	*Pinus thunbergiana*
67	Japanese Red, G9a.	*Pinus densiflora*
68	Japanese White, G16b.	*Pinus parviflora*
66	Lacebark, G4a.	*Pinus bungeana*
68	Limber, G14a.	*Pinus flexilis*
67	Mugo, G8b.	*Pinus mugo*
67	Red, G11b.	*Pinus resinosa*
67	Scotch, G8a.	*Pinus sylvestris*
67	Swiss Mountain, G8b.	*Pinus mugo*
68	Swiss Stone, G16a.	*Pinus cembra*
67	Virginia, G7a.	*Pinus virginiana*
68	White, G15a.	*Pinus strobus*
30	Pipe, Dutchman's, 193a.	*Aristolochia durior*
	Planetree	
51	American, 358a.	*Platanus occidentalis*
51	London, 358b.	*Platanus × acerifolia*
	Plum	
50	Canada, 345a.	*Prunus nigra*
48, 49	Cherry, 335b., 343b.	*Prunus cerasifera*
44	Double Flowering, 297a.	*Prunus triloba* var. *multiplex*
48, 49	Myrobalan, 335b., 343b.	*Prunus cerasifera*
	Poplar	
55	Eastern, 389b.	*Populus deltoides*
55	Lombardy, 389a.	*Populus nigra* 'Italica'
32	Tulip, 207a.	*Liriodendron tulipifera*
43	White, 292a.	*Populus alba*
32	Yellow, 207a.	*Liriodendron tulipifera*
54, 62	Possumhaw, 376b., 435a.	*Ilex decidua*
10	Princess Tree, 35a.	*Paulownia tomentosa*

	Privet	
24	Amur, 142b.	*Ligustrum amurense*
24	Border, 142a.	*Ligustrum obtusifolium*
24	European, 141a.	*Ligustrum vulgare*
20	Golden, 107a.	*Ligustrum × vicaryi*
24	Japanese, 136a.	*Ligustrum japonicum*
7	Rat-stripper, 10a.	*Paxistima canbyi*
31	Redbud, Eastern, 202a.	*Cercis canadensis*
	Redcedar	
73	Colorado, G52b.	*Juniperus scopulorum*
73	Eastern, G55a.	*Juniperus virginiana*
72	Redwood, Dawn, G43a.	*Metasequoia glyptostroboides*
	Rhododendron	
40	Carolina, 266b.	*Rhododendron carolinianum*
40	Catawba, 267a.	*Rhododendron catawbiense*
40	Korean, 268a.	*Rhododendron mucronulatum*
40	P.J.M., 266a.	*Rhododendron* 'P.J.M.'
25, 27	Rose, 147a., 166a.	*Rosa*
44	Rose-of-Sharon, 299a.	*Hibiscus syriacus*
29	Rowan, 180a.	*Sorbus aucuparia*
55	Rubber Tree, 391a.	*Eucommia ulmoides*
31	Russian-olive, 200a.	*Elaeagnus angustifolia*
29	Sandberry, 185b.	*Arctostaphylos uva-ursi*
55	Sarvis-tree, 387b.	*Amelanchier arborea*
34	Sassafras, 222a.	*Sassafras albidum*
27	Scholar-tree, 162a.	*Sophora japonica*
	Serviceberry	
55	Allegheny, 386a.	*Amelanchier laevis*
55	Downy, 387b.	*Amelanchier arborea*
55	Pacific, 385b.	*Amelanchier florida*
55	Saskatoon, 385a.	*Amelanchier alnifolia*
55	Shadblow, 387a.	*Amelanchier canadensis*
55	Service-tree, 387b.	*Amelanchier arborea*
55	Shadbush, 387b.	*Amelanchier arborea*
19	Sheepberry, 101a.	*Viburnum lentago*
57	Silverbell, Carolina, 398b.	*Halesia carolina*
30	Silver Lace Vine, 193b.	*Polygonum aubertii*
41	Smokebush, 273a.	*Cotinus coggygria*
	Smoketree	
41	American, 273b.	*Cotinus obovatus*
41	Common, 273a.	*Cotinus coggygria*
24	Snowberry, 140a., 140b.	*Symphoricarpos albus*

Page	Common name	Scientific name
37, 58	Sorrel Tree, 246a., 404a.	*Oxydendrum arboreum*
37, 58	Sourwood, 246a., 404a.	*Oxydendrum arboreum*
34	Spicebush, 221a.	*Lindera benzoin*
	Spirea	
62	Bridalwreath, 433a.	*Spiraea prunifolia*
65	Bumald, 455a.	*Spiraea* × *bumalda*
64, 65	Japanese, 449b., 455b.	*Spiraea japonica*
62	Snowmound Nippon, 433b.	*Spiraea nipponica* 'Snowmound'
61	Thunberg, 430a.	*Spiraea thunbergii*
44, 60, 65	Vanhoutte, 297b., 421a., 454a.	*Spiraea* × *vanhouttei*
	Spruce	
70	Black Hills, G27b.	*Picea glauca* 'Densata'
70	Blue Colorado, G28a.	*Picea pungens* 'Glauca'
70	Colorado, G28b.	*Picea pungens*
70	Dwarf Alberta, G27a.	*Picea glauca* 'Conica'
69	Norway, G24a.	*Picea abies*
69	Oriental, G25a.	*Picea orientalis*
71	Serbian, G38a.	*Picea omorika*
69	White, G26b.	*Picea glauca*
60	Stephanandra, Cutleaf, 421b.	*Stephanandra incisa*
56, 64	Stewartia, Mountain, 394a., 452a.	*Stewartia ovata*
	St. Johnswort	
20	Golden, 106b.	*Hypericum frondosum*
20	Kalm, 105a.	*Hypericum kalmianum*
20	Shrubby, 106a.	*Hypericum prolificum*
20	Strawberry-shrub, 110a.	*Calycanthus floridus*
36, 57, 58	Sugarberry, 239a., 399b., 410a.	*Celtis laevigata*
	Sumac	
26	Flameleaf, 156a.	*Rhus copallina*
25	Fragrant, 147b.	*Rhus aromatica*
26	Shining, 156a.	*Rhus copallina*
26, 29	Smooth, 157b., 178a.	*Rhus glabra*
26, 29	Staghorn, 157a., 178b.	*Rhus typhina*
60	Sweetfern, 420b.	*Comptonia peregrina*
51	Sweetgum, 360a.	*Liquidambar styraciflua*
20	Sweetshrub, 110a.	*Calycanthus floridus*
51	Sycamore, 358a.	*Platanus occidentalis*
29	Tamarisk, 181a.	*Tamarix*
30	Tara Vine, 194a.	*Actinidia arguta*
28	Tree of Heaven, 171a.	*Ailanthus altissima*

13	Trumpetcreeper, 54a.	*Campsis radicans*
13	Trumpet Vine, 54a.	*Campsis radicans*
32	Tuliptree, 207a.	*Liriodendron tulipifera*
37	Tupelo Black, 242b.	*Nyssa sylvatica*
68	Umbrella-pine, Japanese, G17a.	*Sciadopitys verticillata*
28	Varnish Tree, 170b.	*Koelreuteria paniculata*
	Viburnum	
19	American Cranberrybush, 99b.	*Viburnum trilobum*
18	Arrowwood, 91a.	*Viburnum dentatum*
19	Blackhaw, 103b.	*Viburnum prunifolium*
16	Burkwood, 79a.	*Viburnum × burkwoodii*
16	Carlcephalum, 79b.	*Viburnum × carlcephalum*
16, 20	Chinese Snowball, 76b., 112b.	*Viburnum macrocephalum*
15	Doublefile, 72a.	*Viburnum plicatum* var. *tomentosum*
19	European Cranberrybush, 99a.	*Viburnum opulus*
16, 19	Fragrant, 79b., 103a.	*Viburnum × carlcephalum* and *Viburnum farreri*
16	Judd, 78b.	*Viburnum × juddii*
16	Koreanspice, 78a.	*Viburnum carlesii*
15, 21	Lantanaphyllum, 74b., 113b.	*Viburnum × rhytidophylloides*
15, 21	Leatherleaf, 74a., 113a.	*Viburnum rhytidophyllum*
18	Linden, 96b.	*Viburnum dilatatum*
19	Nannyberry, 101a.	*Viburnum lentago*
19	Sargent, 98a.	*Viburnum sargentii*
19	Siebold, 100a.	*Viburnum sieboldii*
18	Tea, 91b.	*Viburnum setigerum*
16	Wayfaringtree, 76a.	*Viburnum lantana*
19	Witherod, 102a.	*Viburnum cassinoides*
64	Walkingstick, Harry Lauder's, 448a.	*Corylus avellana* 'Contorta'
	Walnut	
28	Black, 174b.	*Juglans nigra*
27, 28	English, 161a., 174a.	*Juglans regia*
27, 28	Persian, 161a., 174a.	*Juglans regia*
15	Weigela, Old Fashioned, 69b.	*Weigela florida*
	Willow	
53	Artic Blue Leaf, 372b.	*Salix purpurea* 'Nana'

53 Corkscrew, Hankow, 373a. — *Salix matsudana* 'Tortuosa'
53 Goat, 369b. — *Salix caprea*
53 Golden Weeping, 374a. — *Salix alba* 'Tristis'
53 Hankow, 373b. — *Salix matsudana*
53 Purpleosier, 372a. — *Salix purpurea*
53 Pussy, 369b. — *Salix discolor*
53 White, 374b. — *Salix alba*
62, 63 Winterberry, Common, 435b., 442a. — *Ilex verticillata*
25 Wisteria, Japanese, 151a. — *Wisteria floribunda*
Witchhazel
45 Chinese, 308a. — *Hamamelis mollis*
45 Common, 309a. — *Hamamelis virginiana*
45 Japanese, 310b. — *Hamamelis japonica*
45 Vernal, 310a. — *Hamamelis vernalis*
56, 61 Yaupon, 392a., 432a. — *Ilex vomitoria*
27 Yellowwood, 161b. — *Cladrastis kentuckia (lutea)*
Yew
71 Anglojap, G42b. — *Taxus* × *media*
71 English, G41a. — *Taxus baccata*
71 Japanese, G42a. — *Taxus cuspidata*
59 Zelkova, Japanese, 413a. — *Zelkova serrata*

REFERENCES

This list includes a variety of types of works ranging from technical identification manuals to more popular works dominated by color photographs.

Bailey, L.H. 1949. *Manual of Cultivated Plants.* Macmillan Co., N.Y.

Bailey Hortorium. 1976. *Hortus III.* Macmillan Co., N.Y.

Cope, E.A. 1986. *Native and Cultivated Conifers of Northeastern North America.* Cornell University Press. Ithaca, N.Y.

DeWolf, G.P., editor. 1987. *Taylor's Guide to Shrubs.* Chanticleer Press, Inc. N.Y.

——. *Taylor's Guide to Trees.* 1988. Houghton Mifflin Co., Boston.

Dirr, M.A. 1978. *Photographic Manual of Woody Landscape Plants.* Stipes Publishing Co., Champaign, IL.

——. 1990. *Manual of Woody Landscape Plants: Their Identification, Ornamental Characteristics, Culture, Propagation and Uses.* Stipes Publishing Co., Champaign, IL.

Everett, T.H. 1980. *The New York Botanical Garden Illustrated Encyclopedia of Horticulture.* Darland STP Press. N.Y.

Gerhold, H.D., W.N. Wandell and N.L. Lacasse. 1993. *Street Tree FactSheets.* Pennstate College of Agricultural Science, Pennsylvania State University, University Park.

Graves, A.H. 1956. *Illustrated Guide to Trees and Shrubs.* Harper and Row. N.Y.

Helmer, J.C. and J.L. Threlkeld. 1979. *Pictorial Library of Landscape Plants.* Vol. I–III. Merchants Publ. Co., Kalamazoo, MI.

Huxley, A. 1992. *Dictionary of Gardening.* Royal Horticultural Society. Vol. I–IV. Stockton Press, N.Y.

Keith, R.H. and F.A. Giles. 1980. *Dwarf Shrubs for the Midwest.* Special Publ. 60. University of Illinois College of Agriculture. Champaign.

Krussmann, G. 1985. *Manual of Cultivated Broad-Leaved Trees and Shrubs.* Vol. I–III. Timber Press. Portland, Oregon.

Krussmann, G. 1985. *Manual of Cultivated Conifers.* Timber Press. Portland, Oregon.

Morrisey, S.I. and F.A. Giles. 1990. *Large Flowering Shrubs for the MIdwest.* Special Publication 74. University Printing Division, University of Illinois. Champaign.

Rehder, A. 1940. *Manual of Cultivated Trees and Shrubs.* 2nd Ed. Macmillan Co. N.Y.

Symonds, G.W.D. 1958. *The Tree Identification Book.* William Morrow & Co. Inc. N.Y.

——. 1963. *The Shrub Identification Book.* M. Barrows & Co. N.Y.

Walker, M.C. and F.A. Giles. 1985. *Flowering Trees for the Midwest.* Univ. of Illinois, Champaign.

Whitcomb, C.E. 1985. *Know It and Grow It.* Lacebark Publications. Stillwater, Oklahoma.

Yiesla, S.A. and F.A. Giles. 1992. *Shade Trees for the Central and Northern United States and Canada.* Stipes Publ. Co., Champaign, Illinois.

NOTES

NOTES

NOTES

NOTES

NOTES

NOTES

NOTES

NOTES

NOTES

NOTES